THE  TIMES

RESTAURANT
GUIDE 2002

First published in the United Kingdom in 2002 by Cassell & Co

Text copyright © Jonathan Meades and Times Newspapers Ltd 2002

A CIP catalogue record for this book is available from the British Library.
ISBN 0 304 35939 4

Every effort has been made to make this guide as accurate as possible at
the time of going to press. It is something of a theme of the book that even
good restaurants come and go with alarming rapidity, particularly in the UK.
As a result, neither *The Times*, the publisher, nor the author can accept any
responsibility for any loss or inconvenience sustained as result of errors or
omissions in the guide. We will, wherever possible, be happy to correct any
errors of fact in subsequent editions. Please direct all such communications
to the publisher.

The numerical score out of ten awarded to each restaurant, however,
is based entirely on the experience of the author on his last visit to the
establishment and is, inevitably, only an opinion, however well founded.
Prices are approximate, for a three-course meal for two, including
modest wine and apéritif.

Art Editor: Austin Taylor
Assistant Editor: Michelle Gustave
Jacket Design by Clive Hayball

Printed and bound in Finland by WS Bookwell, Juva
Typeset in Fairfield and Bembo

Cassell & Co
Wellington House
125 Strand
London, WC2R 0BB

THE TIMES
RESTAURANT
GUIDE 2002

Jonathan Meades

CASSELL&CO

CONTENTS

INTRODUCTION

This guide's entries are drawn from a database established during the 15 years that I contributed a weekly restaurant review to *The Times*. The majority of them are for establishments in Britain, where restaurants tend not to enjoy longevity: the familial base which underpins the restaurant trade throughout most of Europe is the exception in this country. Thus many of the thousand or so places I've written about are no longer with us. Deservedly no longer with us, it might be said. While the standard of British restauration has improved over this past decade and a half the standard of British cooking hasn't kept pace. The sheer number of restaurants has suffered an exponential increase but there has been no commensurate increase in the number of chefs capable of cooking in those places. Notions that British gastronomy has come of age or that London is something called 'the restaurant capital of the world' are wide of the mark and born of collective self-delusion. Were I in the business of marketing restaurants – which I'm not: witness the volume of hostile letters I received down the years – I would bang on about this guide's USP, its Unique Selling Proposition. Since I'm not in marketing, I shall go two better.

The Unique Selling Proposition is that this is all the work of one person. The same criteria – entirely subjective but nonetheless consistent – are applied to restaurants wherever they are to be found: Bordeaux, Bristol, Brussels. There is no other guide which is composed by such a means. Even those which have someone's name on them bear the tell-tale inventory of contributors' names. And as for the others, wrought by 'professional' inspectors, by anonymous postal respondents, by dreary consensus... bum steers, the lot.

The Only Slightly Less Unique Selling Proposition is that many of my British itineraries have been determined not by the ambition to reach this or that 'destination' restaurant but by my TV schedules. Over those 15 years I have spent more than 100 weeks in British provincial hotels in places whose topography, buildings, civil engineering, and so on have fascinated me enough to film them but whose essays in hospitality and restauration were such that much of my diet throughout the period was, perforce, whisky and crisps – Johnny Walker and Walkers if there's no single malt, which there usually isn't, if there are no handcrafted deepfries from artisinal worthies, which there usually aren't. British gastronomic revolution? What a tired joke that seems when you're banged up in Worcester for a month.

The Fairly Unique Selling Proposition is that I have no compunction in biting the hand that feeds. I do not have a place on the gastrobiz carrousel – I keep the trade I write about at arm's length. I have few friends in it, and even those I do have became inured to what they no doubt considered to be a traitorous bluntness. Much writing about restaurants and food – not necessarily the same thing – is a hardly dissembled form of PR. Like most of the rest of the human race, I am biddable. But my price, never reached, was infinitely higher than that of a free lunch.

GREATER LONDON

CENTRAL LONDON

W1

1837 BROWN'S HOTEL   2
32 Albemarle St, London W1 (020) 7408 1837
Pass the door and you are in the provincial England of the late
Fifties and early Sixties. If you're of an age to have eaten in a
posh hotel in Cheltenham or Norwich in those years and wish
to relive that exciting time then, provided your palate hasn't
come on much since then, this could be for you.

L MON TO FRI, D MON TO SAT £140

ALASTAIR LITTLE   9
49 Frith St, London W1 (020) 7734 5183
Little's inspiration for some time has been Italy, an Italy rarely
represented in London. Pasta e ceci is the great soup of
Naples; Little tarts it up with shellfish to achieve real heights.
Beef is poached rare and served with Salsa Verde. Cold oysters
are served with tiny hot sausages. This is currently among the
most satisfying places in London.

L MON TO FRI, D MON TO SAT £100

AROMA II

8

118 Shaftesbury Ave, London W1 (020) 7437 0377

Possesses a deftness that is rare in Chinatown. Delicacy
pervades much of his cooking: a dish of scrambled egg
white with shrimp was excellent. As was sea slug with dried,
powdered shrimp roe, greaselessly fried pig's innards, beef
brisket cooked as 'goulash' and eel roast with a coat of
honey. Drink cold saki served in little crown-corked bottles.

L AND D EVERY DAY. £75+

THE ATLANTIC

6

20 Glasshouse St, London W1 (020) 7734 4888

Vast subterranean labyrinth of bars among which is a
restaurant that, against all the odds, is pretty much the works.
The place is partly Twenties, partly Thirties and has been done
over with a mix of flair and tacky vulgarity which is absolutely
apt for somewhere so close to Piccadilly Circus. It's a wildly
successful enterprise, not least because it stays open until
3am. But the sheer size, too, is attractive. It helps to be young.
The menu is perhaps best sampled at lunchtime, when the
kitchen is not under massive pressure. Foie gras is done with
a potato galette; smoked haddock with lightly fried spinach.
Other decent items include duck confit with smashing fried
potatoes; sea bass with courgette 'spaghetti' and saffron; fennel
tart. Good wines, nice sweets, sullen service.

L MON TO FRI, D EVERY DAY £75+

BACK TO BASICS

5

21a Foley St, London W1 (020) 7436 2181

The daft name might suggest a Majorite Valhalla or some
veggie hell, but it's not like that at all. The German chef is
nicely accomplished. Gravlax is high quality and recommended.
Skate is excellent. The portions are generously German,
determined to make a Kohl of each of us.

L AND D MON TO FRI £80

BAM-BOU

2

1 Percy St, London W1 (020) 7323 9130

A sort of theme restaurant which summons up *The Deer
Hunter*. The premises have been done over with dark wood,
dark sisal carpet. Charming staff are dressed in military
fatigues. The cosmetically Vietnamese food tastes like the
generic orientalism of a European chef who spices too
reticently – spring rolls are insipid; soft-shelled crab is far
from crisp. Crab cakes are pleasant. Noodles, allegedly
flavoured with ginger, taste of nothing.

L MON TO FRI, D MON TO SAT £80+

BICE   5
13 Albemarle St, London W1 (020) 7409 1011
The London link in a chain of smooth Milanese outfits that
extends to Los Angeles, Paris, etc. This is a chic and understated
basement serving food that is subtle or bland according to taste.
Ordinary-sounding things such as breaded veal cutlet are
heightened by the use of first-rate ingredients and by obviously
careful cooking. Also recommended: Vitello Tonnato; tortelloni
stuffed with spinach and ricotta and sauced with clarified butter
and deep-fried sage; turbot cooked in a condom of wafer-thin
potato; gorgonzola with honey and walnuts. The prices are high.

L MON TO FRI, D MON TO SAT £100 (LUNCH IS CHEAPER)

LA CAPANNINA   5
24 Romilly St, London W1 (020) 7437 2473
Chianti bottles on the ceiling, cramped tables and frenetic waiters,
but this is cooking rather than catering. Lovely risotto with porcini.

L MON TO FRI, D MON TO SAT £45

CHAOPRAYA   3
22 St Christopher's Pl, London W1 (020) 7486 0777
Cavernous Thai basement. The spicing is ferocious. Much of
the cooking is impressive: Chinese sugar salad, beef with hot
basil and noodles, etc.

L AND D MON TO SAT £55+

CHEZ GERARD   4
8 Charlotte St, London W1 (020) 7636 4975
Steak and chips. Numerous cuts are offered, all of them
peculiar to French (and Belgian) beef butchery. Onglet is
excellent. Branches everywhere.

L SUN TO FRI, D EVERY DAY £75

CHEZ NICO AT NINETY   9
Grosvenor House Hotel, 90 Park Lane, London W1
(020) 7409 1290
All that one would expect of London's most consistent luxury
restaurateur, though less based in classical procedure than it
used to be.

L MON TO FRI, D MON TO SAT £80

CHUEN CHENG KU   3
17 Wardour St, London W1 (020) 7437 1398
Labyrinth of rooms on three floors. The staff are well-schooled
in rudeness but the dim sum is good.

L AND D EVERY DAY £30

CENTRAL LONDON:W1   11

THE CONNAUGHT   7
16 Carlos Pl, London W1 (020) 7499 7070
The cooking is enjoyable. At least I enjoyed it when I ate it.
Does the Connaught have paramedics standing by? The item
that did for me was a salmi of guinea fowl, truffles and morels.
That I could have coped with. But then there was the cream...

L AND D EVERY DAY £150

THE CRITERION   7
Piccadilly Circus, London W1 (020) 7930 0488
This great late-Victorian Ottoman barn is one of the most
striking public rooms in London. If you can't afford to eat,
go and gawp. This is the least gastronomic of Marco Pierre
White's restaurants: stuffed cabbage, sweetbread beignets,
poached fruit.

L MON TO SAT, D EVERY DAY £90

ELENA'S L'ETOILE   5
30 Charlotte St, London W1 (020) 7636 7189
This restaurant has been around since the beginning of time
and Eleanor Salvoni is now the doyenne of London's greeters.
Pseudo-Chinese duck was overcooked and is best overlooked,
but the breads of a lamb the size of a bull fricassee'd with
peas and spinach was lovely grub.

L MON TO FRI, D MON TO SAT £85

L'ESCARGOT   8
48 Greek St, London W1 (020) 7437 6828
Walls are hung with lithographs by Miró and Chagall. The
kitchen's touch is light – apart from when it is heavy, which
it is with reduction sauces. Both duck and lamb would have
benefited from less exaggerated dark puddles – the meats
themselves were fully flavoured from proper hanging and timed
to the second. Roasted salmon layered with roesti and spinach
was very fine. Foie gras terrine was excellent. Desserts – peach
melba and chocolate tart – showed real expertise.

L MON TO FRI, D MON TO SAT £85+

FIREBIRD   5
23 Conduit St, London W1 (020) 7493 7000
According to the bumf that comes with the bill, this is 'an
authentic pre-revolutionary restaurant'. Which will be why
the nonstop pianist plays Burt Bacharach or Lennon and
McCartney: no wonder the old regime didn't see what was
coming. Cooking is Russian insofar as certain of the ideas
and names are Russian, but that is about as far as it goes.
The techniques, the flair, the balance are classically French.
Stew-like borsch was good. Shaslik is merely lamb fillet in a

middle-eastern mufti, and is accompanied by excellently garlicky rice. Venison is done with swede puree and cherries.

L MON TO FRI, D MON TO SAT £120 (LUNCH IS CHEAPER)

GARBO'S

2

42 Crawford St, London W1 (020) 7262 6582
Swedish cooking, Swedish service (which is doggedly inefficient), Swedish clientele, Swedish pop music. The 'national dish', Jansson's Temptation (a gratin of potato, anchovies and cream) is not notably well done. But there's good smoked eel cooked in beer, meatballs in cream and Pripp beer.

L SUN TO FRI, D MON TO SAT £55+

THE GAUCHO GRILL

4

19 Swallow St, London W1 (020) 7734 4040
For the design-conscious gaucho: a cellar full of butch wrought metal, door handles shaped like horns and the pelt of a whole herd of Fresians on the banquettes. Argentinian steaks are properly hung and succulent. The garnish with them is redundant. Other offerings include grilled sweetbreads, grilled provolone cheese, mild chorizo.

L AND D EVERY DAY £70+

LE GAVROCHE

10

43 Upper Brook St, London W1 (020) 7408 0881/7499 1826
What a burden to succeed your father when your father is Albert Roux. Surely it's better to take up the law or something? We should be delighted he didn't. Michel A. Roux's cooking belongs to the school of cooking called supremely good cooking. Dish after dish after dish displayed the balanced, undemonstrative perfection that only the greatest restaurants achieve. A quadripartite pig plate comprises hot charcuterie in the form of ballotine, loin, incredibly sweet ventrèche and hot crackling. Poached duck was of quite startling excellence. There is a massive selection of cheeses, including a hot goat cheese cooked in pastry. The wines are quite something, too.

L AND D MON TO FRI £150 (SET LUNCH £90)

THE GAY HUSSAR

5

2 Greek St, London W1 (020) 7437 0973
The only Hungarian restaurant left in central London. A railway carriage of a place that's not nearly as club-like as its reputation supposes. The cooking is generally pretty good: smoked goose with smoked beans; cold pike with various salads and relishes. Iffy wines.

L AND D MON TO SAT £80

GOPAL'S

4

12 Bateman St, London W1 (020) 7434 1621
Smart Indian restaurant with very smart cooking. Good
'patties' of herbed potato, good tandoor cooked meats.

L AND D EVERY DAY £30

GORDON RAMSAY AT CLARIDGE'S

9

Brook St, London W1 (020) 7499 0099
The restaurant is truly glamorous. It is a very rare example of
English repro art deco: the style of the 1925 exhibition rather
than that of the Hoover factory. It and Gordon Ramsay are
lucky to have each other. Ramsay is currently London's best
haute cuisinier and he has created an old restaurant. The
potent delicacy of his cooking is quite at odds both with
English tradition and current London practice. It is not out
of the mould. The persistent impressions are of mental and
manual agility, of confident balance, of a trust in the
customer's palate. There is also a manifest desire to please.
The staff are solicitous rather than importunate. What to eat?
Just about everything.

L AND D EVERY DAY £120

HAKKASAN

1

8 Hanway Pl, London W1 (020) 7907 1888
The ill-lit wide stone staircase is perhaps the most potentially
perilous entrance to any London restaurant. I have not been
to a state-of-the-art nightclub in the new Shanghai but there's
no reason to suppose that such a place would be much
different to this. Pounding pop music drives you up the wall.
The kitchen is over-reliant on deep-frying, a technique it has
yet to master.

L AND D TUES TO SUN £110

HARBOUR CITY

5

46 Gerrard St, London W1 (020) 7439 7859
Some of the better made dim sum in Soho. Dishes are ordered
from a menu, not from a trolley. The choice is dauntingly long,
more than 100 items. These include such things as beef
intestines, pig skin and turnip in soup, duck tongues in chilli
and black beans. But what sets it above its competitors is the
finesse with which more conventional dishes are handled.

L AND D EVERY DAY £30+

HARD ROCK CAFE   2
150 Old Park La, London W1 (020) 7629 0382
A touristic institution. As well as a restaurant it is a monument
to the early Seventies taste for anything to do with the Fifties
and, further, it is a museum of rock and roll memorabilia –
which means lots of guitars and photos. The basic cooking is
hard on the digestion, though easy on the pocket, given the
vast quantities that are dished up. Burgers are disappointing
but the chilli con carne and the steaks are all right.

L AND D EVERY DAY £42

HARRY'S BAR   10
26 South Audley St, London W1 (020) 7408 0844
Some of the most exquisite cooking in London is served in
this private club for film stars of the old school, Mayfair
dandies and the gastronomically earnest. Alberico Penati
remains a genuine and rare article, a consummate practitioner
whose bases in his native cooking are discernible (he comes
from Bergamo), but who remains untrammelled by the
precedents of Mama's cooking. The unusually long menu
includes tripe done in a terrine wrapped in cabbage leaf;
borlotti beans with langoustines; excellent broad bean risotto;
thin, flat pasta sauced with chicken livers; monkfish with
clams. Peripheral items – crudites, butter, grissini – are
treated with the same care as the centrepieces.

L AND D MON TO FRI £160+

IBLA   4
89 Marylebone High St, London W1 (020) 7224 3799
The Italian chef seems intent on copying the English, who
copied the French. He is overinterested in the way a dish
looks, is prone to pile on components which add nothing,
and is fond of exaggeratedly reduced sauces. Some dishes
come off reasonably well, however – monkfish with battered
courgette 'chips' and a sauce of pureed aubergine; sweetbreads
roasted with provolone. The lighting is designed to pick out
every open pore.

L AND D MON TO SAT £75

IKKYU   6
67 Tottenham Court Rd, London W1 (020) 7636 9280
Informal and rather chaotic Japanese basement cafe
specialising in rustic cooking. Much of this is very good
indeed: potato and beef stew, grilled pickerel, meaty-tasting
miso soup, wonderful sashimi in large portions, grilled duck.

L MON TO FRI, D SUN TO FRI £30

ITSU SOHO

4

103 Wardour St, London W1 (020) 7479 4794

Little of this restaurant's repertoire is Japanese. 'New style sashimi' is actually thin slices of salmon in a bath of groundnut oil, ginger and sesame. This was most pleasing. As was traditional sashimi. Salmon tartar was assaulted by soya sauce. Hijiki chicken is delicious – the bird's breast was succulent, sliced and dressed with a vinaigrette based on English mustard. Miso soup is to be avoided.

L AND D EVERY DAY £40+

JIMMY'S

0

23 Frith St, London W1 (020) 7437 9521

The Isthmian league of Cypriot kebab cookery conducted in a nicotine-stained cellar, where the atmosphere of old Soho is plastered on impasto.

L AND D MON TO SAT £30

KASPIA

4

18 Bruton Pl, London W1 (020) 7493 2612

Snack bar for the very rich; caviar, champagne, vodka and foie gras served in rather club-like surroundings in a Mayfair mews.

L AND D MON TO SAT £100

LEVANT

5

Jason Court, 76 Wigmore St, London W1 (020) 7224 1111

Levant's cooking is Levantine in the way the River Cafe's is Italian. That is to say, it's inspired by the eastern Mediterranean with a nod to further east still and to north Africa. Taramasalata was overpoweringly metallic, but what followed was pretty well judged. Brochettes of lamb offal were splendid. Long-roast kid served with its juices is one-pot cooking at its best. The breads, leavened and unleavened, are terrific. Drink arak or lassi.

L MON TO FRI, D EVERY DAY £72

THE LEXINGTON

5

Lexington St, London W1 (020) 7434 3401

Smart, understated, sassy outfit in west Soho. The cooking lurches from one pole to the other. At its best, it competes with the big boys. At its worst, it's poor. Portions throughout are gargantuan. A fricassee of lamb offal is so good that it could become a London classic. And the puddings, such as a sampler plate called The Full Monte, are excellent. Good wines at good prices.

L MON TO FRI, D MON TO SAT £60

MARCO PIERRE WHITE AT THE OAK ROOM

10

Le Meridien Hotel, 21 Piccadilly, London W1
(020) 7734 8000

White has always been a cautious craftsman with a disinclination to experiment in front of his audience. But that does not mean that his repertoire and techniques are immutable. His current menu draws its inspiration from the canon of old and grand French classicism. The right note is struck over and over again. There is no resort to embellishment; there is total trust in integration, fine ingredients, spot-on timing, perfect balance, lightness of touch. Lobster, grilled, excised from the shell, cut up, replaced in the shell with a bath of garlic butter, lightly glazed with béarnaise, was marvellous. So was pigeon – ungamey, mild, sweet, on hardly acidulated choucroûte with a sauce enriched with truffles and foie gras.

L MON TO FRI, D MON TO SAT £150

MASH

4

19-21 Great Portland St, London W1 (020) 7637 5555

Polyglot cooking that has become a tiresome London norm. An oversweet, overchilli'd pizza with a sprinkling of balsamic vinegar was unimpressive. Lamb with broad beans, peas, braised lettuce and mint was more successfuly integrated.

L AND D MON TO SAT £65+

MEZZO

7

100 Wardour St, London W1 (020) 7314 4000

Massively hyped and massively massive. The basement restaurant seats 350, sports a cigarette girl, a formidably well-drilled staff, an almost palpable confidence and the sort of sexiness that only Conran can buy. This place is louchely glamorous, not quite respectable. It's futile to pretend that the cooking is the point, but it's cracking. The best: sweet lamb rump with turnip gratin; beef fillet with bone marrow and a buttery crouton; onion tart; tomato custard tart (extraordinary); breadcrumbed pig's trotter; orange bavarois.

L WED TO FRI AND SUN, D EVERY DAY £100

MING

7

33-36 Greek St, London W1 (020) 7734 2721

Some of the most engaging Chinese cooking in London is served here. Recommended: the slow-cooked dishes, especially the two based on belly pork; prawns in a bean-curd batter; anything deep-fried. Proper selection of wines.

L AND D MON TO SAT £55

MIRABELLE   9
56 Curzon St, London W1 (020) 7499 4636

Marco Pierre White has learnt how to give good restaurant. On
the face of it a protracted dungeon beneath an undistinguished
block of service flats, the dining rooms are lent glamour by just
a few judicious touches – a mirrored hanging globe, 1940s
mirrored screens. The food is fabulous. 'Roast chicken (for
two)' is as good as any roast chicken I've ever tasted. This is
due to the quality of the fowl, the quality of the persillade,
which is stuffed between the breast and its skin and the
quality of the risotto it is served with. Omelette Arnold
Bennett is soufflé-like light and eggy. Fourme d'Ambert is
sensational. Excellent Bullshot.

L AND D EVERY DAY, BRUNCH AT WEEKENDS £100

MOMO   8
25 Heddon St, London W1 (020) 7434 4040

The designers have lifted liberally from the sculpted mud
vernacular of southern Morocco, Mali, the Hoggar and,
especially from the work of the Egyptian modernist, Hassan
Fathy. This is among the most ambitious and gastronomically
satisfying north African restaurants in London. Among the
many fine dishes: pastilla, marinated sardines, brochette of
lamb offal, mechouia, a fabulous tajine of duck, cinnamon
and apples. And the couscous is a revelation.

L AND D EVERY DAY £80

MORTON'S   6
28 Berkeley Sq, London W1 (020) 7499 0363

Good site overlooking Berkeley Square. There is no coarseness,
and no forcing of flavours. Roast belly pork with ceps and
girolles – roast to finish it and render it crisp – had previously
been braised to the state of pork ointment, like hot rillettes.
Three Yorkshire puddings, served with a thick round of perfect
entrecote, are filled with roast foie gras, fried ceps and ferrous
spinach. The cheeses come with proper homemade biscuits.

L MON TO FRI, D EVERY DAY £100

LE MUSCADET   5
25 Paddington St, London W1 (020) 7935 2883

An old-fashioned bistro. The choice of wines is poor and
vintages and makers are often not specified. The
middle-of-the-road cooking is competently executed. Foie gras
is fried and served with apples and madeira sauce. Smoked
duck breast and rillettes appear in a salad. Boned rabbit is
stuffed with prunes. Duck confit is served without its skin.
The all French cheeses come from Olivier of Boulogne.

L MON TO FRI, D MON TO SAT £85

NADINE'S

2

23-24 Greek St, London W1 (020) 7439 1063

Not really a couscous house at all but a Lebanese restaurant posing as an Algerian one. The meze is perfectly all right, the couscous is uninspired.

L AND D EVERY DAY £40+

NEW WORLD

2

1 Gerrard Pl, London W1 (020) 7734 0677

One of the largest restaurants in London – it seats more than 500 people and most of them are Chinese. At lunchtime, when they do quite decent dim sum from trolleys, you can believe yourself in Hong Kong.

L AND D EVERY DAY £30

NICOLE'S

1

158 New Bond St, London W1 (020) 7499 8408

Very good-looking outfit in the basement of the rag trader Nicole Farhi's store. Service is sweet-natured and swift. The cooking though, resembles Ms Farhi's clothes – safe, understated, often rather boring. The kitchen seems desperate not to offend with flavour. It is also amiss in some of it's timing. Virtually every dish displays mistakes. Duck confit, which is flaccid, is served with a white bean puree, which is flavourless. Grilled veg are undercooked. Calf's liver is overcooked. Crème Catalan is nasty.

L MON TO SAT, D MON TO FRI £90+

THE O'CONOR DON

1

88 Marylebone Lane, London W1 (020) 7935 9311

The pleasingly shabby first-floor dining room of an Edwardian pub. Strong on ambience, weak on food – some of which is inexcusably inept. The Irish stew is ghastly, cooked with meat that is unsuited to long and over-enthusiastic boiling. Hot buttered oysters are OK. Black treacle tart is unexciting.

L AND D MON TO FRI £60

L'ODEON

8

65 Regent St, (entrance in Air St) London W1
(020) 7287 1400

Long, low narrow room. Immaculate boiled beef with sauce verte and pork knuckle with boulangère potatoes are fabulous, among the best examples of this sort of cooking in London. Also unmissable: a terrine of foie gras and terrine done with quatre épices; scallops with girolles, Parmesan wafers and persillade cream; extraordinary beef tartare. The desserts are tip-top.

L AND D MON TO SAT £100, SET LUNCH £50+

THE ORIENTAL

2

The Dorchester, Park Lane, London W1 (020) 7629 8888
Outrageous prices for moderate cooking. It might work in
Brussels or Geneva, but London has the best oriental
restaurants in Europe – so this one is redundant. A champagne
cocktail costs £8.50. Eight thin slices of abalone with broccoli
were £17.50. Presentation is formal and fussy. Flavours are
persistently quiet. The wine list, which is shared with the
hotel's other restaurants, is first-class. Set menus range from
£45 to £90 per person.

L MON TO FRI, D MON TO SAT £140+

ORIGINAL TAJINE

8

7a Dorset St, London W1 (020) 7935 1545
The kitchen provides a masterclass in Moroccan cooking. It
would be invidious to point to a particular dish as the absolute
tops for there are so many which hit the spot. Pastilla is done
in a flat version, here filled with chicken sandwiched between
layers of the crispest sugared pastry. The salads are rich and
delicious – lamb's kidneys are the centrepiece of one.
Couscous with mixed grilled meats could not be improved.
The same must be said of a tajine of lamb and pears.

L MON TO FRI, D MON TO SAT £50

OZER

7

4 Langham Pl, London W1 (020) 7323 0505
This restaurant pronounces itself as 'modern Ottoman', which
turns out to mean high-quality French cooking with a faint
Turkish accent. It is as different from the London-Turkish
restaurants of Stoke Newington or Green Lanes as is the Ritz
from a country pub. The chef, Jerome Tauvron, is a gifted
original. Two mullet dishes were exquisite: the first was done
with deep-fried herbs and tuna puree, the second with smoked
aubergine 'caviar' and potato crisps. Fondant quoits of
deliciously savoury lamb come with hazelnuts and a couture-
dressed salad. One dessert was more Turkish than French –
'eggs' of a sweet nutty mix rather like sugared falafel.

L MON TO FRI, D MON TO SAT £85

PATOGH

6

8 Crawford Pl, London W1 (020) 7262 4015
Unlike most of the cafes in this area, this is Persian rather than
Lebanese. There are a few dip things like yoghurt with shallots
or cucumber and hummus to start, then a choice of about four
grills. The minced lamb kufteh kebab is splendid; organic
chicken and lamb kebabs are just as good. Bread is superb:
unleavened, the circumference of a car tyre, and speckled with
seeds. Drink 'yoghurt drink'.

L AND D EVERY DAY £30+ (NO ALCOHOL BYO)

Pizzeria Condotti   2
4 Mill St, London W1 (020) 7499 1308
Bustling, smart place hung with indifferent 1970s prints. Drink
Peroni beer or champagne, there's little in between to bother with.

L AND D MON TO SAT £45

Planet Hollywood   0
13 Coventry St, London W1 (020) 7287 1000
Planet Hollywood is ill-named. Planet MTV would be more
apt. Planet Trash would be aptest. The Hollywood it celebrates
is not that of Welles or Siodmak or Coppola but that of aes-
thetic midgets with big budgets. The genius of the place is that
it replicates the way that tracksuit bottoms eat at home. You
can come here and eat couch-potato-style grot while gaping
at a screen. You don't even have to button-punch.

L AND D EVERY DAY £50

la Porte des Indes   3
32 Bryanston St, London W1 (020) 7224 0055
Labyrinthine place specialising in the cooking of the former
French territories of Pondicherry and Hyderabad.

L SUN TO FRI, D EVERY DAY, SUNDAY BRUNCH £90+

Quo Vadis   8
26-29 Dean St, London W1 (020) 7437 9585
The dining room is decorated with Emily Mayer's and Marco
Pierre White's Hirst pastiches, which are Damien-Lite. The
cooking has the high gloss and fierce precision that White's
places invariably possess. The menu is almost a bistro's. Dishes
tend toward simplicity and are impeccably judged: beignets of
aubergine and courgette in a beer batter; a fantastically
delicate risotto with squid tentacles; sweet lamb rack; chips
that are almost soufflé-like.

L MON TO FRI, D MON TO SAT £100 PLUS

RK Stanleys   6
6 Little Portland St, London W1 (020) 7462 0099
The interior recalls late-Fifties Salisbury Woolies, with a
soupçon of early Wimpy bar and a hint of bus station caff –
knowingly unknowing. The room is divided by a bar, which
has high tech keg pumps as well as real beers, Dunkerton's
ciders, Somerset apple brandies, unfiltered apple juice. Glazed
bacon knuckle was copious and cheap. The accompaniments
included mash and pease pudding, both of them first-rate,
caramelised pears, gently pickled sauerkraut and a top-notch
pork sausage. Meatloaf was really good.

L AND D MON TO SAT £50

RAGAM   2
57 Cleveland St, London W1 (020) 7636 9098
A rare London restaurant specialising in the cooking of Kerala,
the southern Malabar coast. The unfamiliar menu includes a
sweet and sour mango dish called kaaldan. Otherwise there
are run-of-the-mill curries and decent south Indian
confections, such as the lentil cakes called masala vadai.
Fine kulfi and lassi.

L AND D EVERY DAY £25

RASA   7
6 Dering St, London W1 (020) 7629 1346
Embassy for the vegetarian food of Kerala. The kitchen cooks
with finesse, refinement, nous. It is the sort of stuff which will
appeal to those who are unfond of generically 'Indian food'.
There are delicately battered deep-fried aubergines and lightly
spiced lentil fritters. The curries are as much herbed as spiced
– each is dependent upon a different masala or spice mix.

L AND D MON TO SAT £65+

RASA SAMUDRA   4
5 Charlotte St, London W1 (020) 7637 0222
The interior is odd and slightly discomforting. The door from
the street opens straight into the first of a series of maze-like
dining rooms. The thing about this place is the addition of fish
dishes to the outstanding Keralan vegetarian cooking practised
at its two siblings. Spicing is unquestionably more arresting
than at the other Rasas; in certain instances it is a near assault.
Beware, then, squid fried with chilli, and lemon sole with chilli
and tamarind. Preprandial pickles are well made – as is
adipoli paratha, a thin bread stuffed with chopped fish.

L EVERY DAY, D MON TO SAT £75

RICHARD CORRIGAN AT LINDSAY HOUSE   7
21 Romilly St, London W1 (020) 7439 0450
Corrigan is a versatile operator whose repertoire is always
carnal, always includes innards and extremities. For instance:
a risotto with veal kidney and crisp batons of pig's ear; ravioli
stuffed with osso buco; sweetbreads dusted with fine crumbs
and roasted whole.

L MON TO FRI, D MON TO SAT £110

THE RITZ

8

150 Piccadilly, London W1 (020) 7493 8181
The dining room is peerless, and entirely French – light,
sprightly, gay and sort of rococo. It's a stage set for a fête
gallante. Nonetheless, it is the most English of grand hotels –
a quality that is perhaps ascribable to its dandyish managing
director, Sir Giles Shepard. The cooking has its ups and
downs, and the old-fashioned silver service is out of kilter with
the modernish menu. Reliable dishes include spiced crab cake,
truffle risotto, lemon tart.

L AND D EVERY DAY £110

SAKURA

3

9 Hanover St, London W1 (020) 7629 2961
One of several Japanese businesses in this quarter of the West
End of London. Large, characterless, but good value and pretty
efficient at lunchtime.

L AND D EVERY DAY £33

SARTORIA

5

20 Savile Row, London W1 (020) 7534 7000
Suits by big-name tailors are shown in bespoke display
windows rather in the manner of an 'international' hotel lobby.
The place displays the restraint and understatement which
you'll find in bougeois restaurants all over Italy. Cooking
recalls the part of Italy called Hammersmith. It is the school
of River Café, Italianate, Italianish. The River Café policy of
buying the very best is followed with happy results: raw ham,
coppa and salami are delicious. A risotto with soupy stewed
rabbit was proper stuff. Lamb was tender but didn't taste of
anything. Scallops with broad beans, peas and rocket was
very good.

L MON TO SAT, D EVERY DAY £110+

SOHO SPICE

4

124/126 Wardour St, London W1 (020) 7434 0808
High-quality Indian cooking at low prices. The profit must be
generated by the sheer number of bums on seats. Despite the
semblance of chaos, the place runs efficiently enough and
service is swift. Main courses are served as a thali – a series
of small dishes of which only the main one varies.

L AND D EVERY DAY £40

SOTHEBY'S: THE CAFE   6
34 New Bond St, London W1 (020) 7293 5077
Charming, polished and rather unexpected. The dining room
is just past the auction house's reception and is the size and
shape of a railway carriage. The design is restrained and
elegant. Punters are more mixed than one might expect:
veteran bimbos, conmen in blazers, inbred Etonians but also
sundry browsers, students, art tourists. Caroline Crumby cooks
with a sure touch: hot smoked eel with lentils and warm potato
salad; deep-fried sardine with tomato salsa; lamb and aubergine
stew with pourgouri; lemon syllabub with macaroons. Fine,
predominantly British cheeses from Neal's Yard.

L SUN TO FRI £55+

SPOON+   1
The Sanderson, 50 Berners St, London W1
(020) 7300 1444
The Philippe Starck interior is a triumph of neo-surrealism:
the colours, the shapes, the tricks of scale are inspiring. The
restaurant is something else. The particularly pointless conceit
is that you 'create your own dishes' by matching a main
ingredient with an accompaniment and a sauce. The food is
not without merit. Prices are absurd, going on indecent.

L AND D EVERY DAY £160+

THE SQUARE   7
6-10 Bruton St, London W1 (020) 7495 7100
Polished, urbane, grown-up and possessed of a decorative
neutrality which makes it difficult to date. Chef Philip Howard is
certainly not scared of flavour – roast foie gras with muscat grapes
and thinly sliced endive was first-rate; veal could not be faulted.
The ratio of (well-drilled, obliging) staff to customers is high.

L MON TO FRI, D EVERY DAY £140

SRI SIAM   4
16 Old Compton St, London W1 (020) 7434 3544
Thai cooking done with European flair - and all the better for it.

L MON TO SAT, D EVERY DAY £60

TAMARIND   5
20 Queen St, London W1 (020) 7629 3561
Slickly designed Mayfair basement; polished Indian cooking by
the former chef of the Oberoi in New Delhi. The menu is short
and many of the dishes are extremely rich – 'black' dahl is
formidably intense; chicken livers with tomato and mild spices
are also attention grabbing. Good-quality ingredients result in
such things as tandoori chicken far surpassing the norm.

L SUN TO FRI, D EVERY DAY £80

TECA   5
54 Brook's Mews, London W1 (020) 7495 4774
Italian outfit at the end of a wide Mayfair mews. It's not so
much minimalist as undecorated. There are bare boards,
turquoise chairs, brown banquettes. 'Steamed' beef displayed
the qualities of poached meat and was wonderful cooking.
The cut was fillet, the timing spot-on. Strips of roast rabbit
with an impeccably dressed salad was neat and clean.

L MON TO FRI, D MON TO SAT £80

TERRACE   2
Le Meridien Hotel, 21 Piccadilly, London W1
(020) 7734 8000
The Parisian chef Michael Rostang is operating a concession
in competition with Marco Pierre White in the Oak Room on
the ground floor. There is no contest. Oysters are gratinated
and served on a mix of tough basmati rice in the shell and
with the shell – there were shards everywhere. Scallops were
mugged by cumin. A decent veal cutlet is grilled with Fourme
d'Ambert. Rocket salad smothered in balsamic vinegary syrup
is nasty. The staff don't have much to do save to interrupt every
conversation to ask: 'Is everything all right?' No, it isn't.

L AND D EVERY DAY £90

LA TROUVAILLE   6
12a Newburgh St, London W1 (020) 7287 8488
The name means a discovery, in the sense of both a find
and an invention. This is certainly a find. There has been
no attempt to bring the interior up to date; some attempt
is made to lay on 'Frenchness' – a couple of the waiters
are accordian-operatives and burst now and again into
self-accompanied song. The cooking is spirited, resourceful,
thrifty. There's abundant use of cheap cuts: a tartine
of pig's trotter, crisp pork belly, veal breast stuffed with
forcemeat.

L AND D MON TO SAT £55

VASCO AND PIERO'S PAVILION   5
15 Poland St, London W1 (020) 7437 8774
Good-looking neo-Regency dining room, fairly ordinary but
completely competent Italian cooking: calf's liver with sage,
steak with green peppercorns, vitello tonnato, etc.

L MON TO FRI, D MON TO SAT £70+

VEERASWAMY
4

99-101 Regent St, London W1 (020) 7734 1401
London's first luxury Indian restaurant, which predated the
curry house onslaught of the Fifties by three decades, has
been reinvigorated.

L AND D EVERY DAY £70

VILLANDRY
3

170 Great Portland St, London W1 (020) 7631 3131
It looks minimal, i.e., done on the cheap, rather than minimalist.
The floor is untreated concrete, the white walls undecorated, save
for copper light sconces; the tables are from junk shops and the
chairs from churches. There is no skimping in the kitchen, however. The quality of ingredients is considered more important than
presentation. Scallops with a stew of lentils, diced carrots and a
dandelion salad was decent, copious. Onion tart, though rather
grey, was first rate. The bread is good and the butter of rare quality.

L EVERY DAY, D MON TO SAT £80

WINDOWS ON THE WORLD
8

London Hilton Hotel, 22 Park Lane, London W1
(020) 7493 8000
Jacques Rolancey, the Lyonnais chef, is truer to his native
cooking than he is to the imperatives of international hotel
practice. His lack of fancy is remarkable. Flavours are
confidently unexaggerated. Scallops with white truffle and
balsamic vinegar are excellent. Cannelloni is stuffed with a light
spinach and herb mixture sauced with a vegetable jus. Bresse
chicken is made into a sort of ballotine, stuffed with a great
forcemeat made out of more chicken, foie gras and truffles.

L SUN TO FRI, D MON TO SAT £140

YATRA
2

34 Dover St, London W1 (020) 7493 0200
Even without a waywardly overpriced and very poor dish
of miserably portioned morels and button mushrooms in a
brick-red sauce the bill would have been outrageous. But one
is paying for the pretension – 'Yatra is an ancient Sanskrit word
meaning sacred pilgrimage', the menu tells us – for the velvet
pillow on every plate, for the Bollywood muzak.

L MON TO FRI, D MON TO SAT £95+

YO! SUSHI

3

52 Poland St, London W1 (020) 7287 0443

The friendly face of fast food – a large and apparently chaotic conveyor belt outfit offering sushi and sashimi on colour-coded plates. The relentless TV theme music is hardly a plus and the tables (as opposed to the serpentine bar) are to be avoided.

ALL DAY EVERY DAY £25+

YOISHO

5

33 Goodge St, London W1 (020) 7323 0477

Japanese canteen offering robust country cooking – beef stew with potato, etc. Sashimi is better than it looks; excellent, if initially off-putting raw salmon with seaweed. Among the best of a generation of Japanese restaurants that is more concerned with cooking than folklore.

L AND D MON TO SAT £50

ZEINA

5

9 Market Pl, London W1 (020) 7323 0776

A couple of minutes and a world away from Oxford Circus. It is Maroc-themed. Velvet bellows, cushions, hookahs for a post-prandial smoke of tobacco sweetened with such agents as rose essence. When the cooking's good, it's well good. A tagine of chicken with olives, preserved lemons and potatoes was impressive, and the grills are first-rate. There is a small selection of Moroccan wines.

L AND D MON TO SAT £45

ZEN CENTRAL

3

20 Queen St, London W1 (020) 7629 8089

The style is Corbusian kitsch, 'functional' in appearance rather than utilitarian. This is a Chinese restaurant determined to show it's not a Soho cheapie; to this end unremarkable dishes are given remarkably high prices. The best efforts are actually not Chinese but Japanese and Thai: sashimi and fishcakes respectively.

L AND D EVERY DAY £70

ZINC BAR AND GRILL

2

21 Heddon St, London W1 (020) 7255 8899

A good-looking place with an appropriately extended bar, glass screens, an open kitchen fronted with grey vitreous mosaic tiles. The cooking is littered with errors of both conception and execution. The simple things are the best bets. Oysters, of course, and more unusually, whitebait. Steak was all right, chips were so-so, béarnaise was hopeless. A leek, pancetta and cheese tart was dire, like a chalky savoury cheesecake on leaden pastry.

L EVERY DAY, D MON TO SAT £70+

WC1

CIGALA

6

54 Lamb's Conduit St, London WC1 (020) 7405 1717

Jake Hodges spent much of his childhood in southern Spain, so his devotion to a repertoire which draws predominantly on Andalucian and Murcian practice has proper foundations. It tends to an almost uncannily naturalistic accuracy in its representations of Spanish practices. This means that certain dishes will be characterised by slapdash approximations. The food is robust, punchily savoury, simply presented: squid with a piquant sauce; soupy fish stew; cooked sardines marinated in escabeche; good bread (which is not a Spanish norm).

L EVERY DAY, D MON TO SAT £70

PIZZA EXPRESS

4

30 Coptic St, London WC1 (020) 7636 3232

The first Pizza Express I went to (in March 1969). I suspect, but can evidently not prove, that the pizzas have diminished in size – no doubt in inverse proportion to the chain's exponential expansion. But the quality is still acceptable (at this branch) and the people waiting were civil and efficient.

L AND D EVERY DAY £35

WAGAMAMA

2

4 Streatham St, London WC1 (020) 7323 9223

Minimalist canteen. Astonishingly cheap Japanese cooking, which is reminiscent of Chinese cooking of the chop-suey era. Most dishes are based on noodles. The snack-like first courses, such as grilled dumplings and spare ribs, are good. You sit at long refectory-type tables.

NOON–11PM MON TO SAT 12.30–10PM SUN £25

WC2

ADMIRALTY

7

Somerset House, Strand, London WC2 (020) 7845 4646

After several changes of kitchen staff, this is now impressive. While the interior will always suggest that its designers were inhibited by the task of working in a Grade I listed building, there is no doubt that the latest chef, Morgan Meunier, is the real thing. His cooking is wholly reliant on French precedent and mostly reliant on French produce. A raviolo of snails with pine nuts was tremendous. Roast bass with lobster sauce was pretty good, too. Dessert was a truly outstanding pineapple and orange soufflé with a pineapple sorbet. Drink: Matha's Marcillac.

L EVERY DAY, D MON TO SAT £100+

ALFRED

7

245 Shaftesbury Ave, London WC2 (020) 7240 2566
Good-looking joint at the junction with New Oxford Street;
the interior is all thunder grey and Cambridge blue. The
selection of bottled British beers is peerless. The wine list is
weaker. The food is splendid. Follows the Gary Rhodes path
and rehabilitates the recidivists of the English repertoire.
Thus, toad-in-the-hole is rendered not only edible but actually
delicious. Bacon is braised and finished with a molasses crust.
Rabbit is braised in Marston's Union Mild. There are fiery
chutneys, and fiery eaux de vie from Somerset. Good
puddings, fine English cheeses.

L AND D MON TO SAT £60

AXIS

1

1 Aldwych, London WC2 (020) 7300 0300
London's first fascist theme restaurant is buried, like some
grubby secret, in a basement's basement. The cooking combines pretension, gormlessness and a misplaced confidence
born of ignorance. Prawn cocktail was indistinguishable from
petrol-station sandwich filling. Jersey royal and smoked bacon
soup tasted like dishwater with scum additive.

L MON TO FRI, D MON TO SAT £100

BANK

9

1 Kingsway, Aldwych, London WC2 (020) 7379 9797
The most colourful of the Nineties mega-restaurants – a
winning combination of new metropolitan standards and
French bourgeois favourites. Stuffed cabbage is terrific. So
is ox cheek braised in red wine with roast root veg. Oysters
are poached and served with a lightish curry sauce and a
sweet onion marmalade; lobster is fried and served with
noodles dressed in lime leaf oil; linguini are sauced with
crab and chilli. The wines are affordable.

L AND D EVERY DAY £65, SET LUNCH £50

BELGO CENTRAAL

4

50 Earlham St, London WC2 (020) 7813 2233
For sheer drama this takes some beating. The designer,
Ron Arad, has pulled off a tour de force: part brico, part
boiler-room retro, wholly imaginative. The cooking is a trawl
through the entire Belgian repertoire with the regrettable
exception of horsemeat. Cuisine à la biere, mussel dishes,
three kinds of waterzooi, three kinds of croquette. And then
there are 100 Belgian beers and dozens of genevers.

ALL DAY, EVERY DAY £50+

BERTORELLI'S
4

44a Floral St, London WC2 (020) 7836 3969

Large, populous place that bears a famous name but cooks better than that name ever did. Mealy, haggis-like black pudding is served with glazed pears and a mustardy dressing. Warm goat's cheese (of excellent quality) is served with artichoke. Guinea fowl is served with rather dissapointing polenta. Chargrilling sometimes means charburning. Good frites and aubergine beignets. Interesting southern Italian wines.

L AND D MON TO SAT £60

CAFE DU JARDIN
5

28 Wellington St, London WC2 (020) 7836 8769

Diffident staff, no-style decor – all too typically Covent Garden. The chef-proprietor is prone to pan-global gimmickry: e.g., a 'Japanese omelette' that comprises seaweed, shredded duck and mushrooms on a thin eggy base. But he can also cook marvellous game dishes such as salmis of hare – a pungent, succulent concoction of real merit. The magret of duck with braised cabbage and pommes Anna is also a winner.

L AND D EVERY DAY £70

CHRISTOPHER'S
7

18 Wellington St, London WC2 (020) 7240 4222

Christopher Gilmour's carnal homage to the Chicagoan grills he frequented when he worked in that city. The kitchen exhibits confidence, conjuring up bold flavours by not getting in the way of first-rate ingredients – the flavour and texture of the steaks here rivals the best that Argentina has to offer. The chips are good, too.

L EVERY DAY, D MON TO SAT £95+

L'ESTAMINET
7

14 Garrick St, London WC2 (020) 7379 1432

The sort of French restaurant that one imagines France is full of, but isn't. Bourgeois, comforting, devoid of pretension. The menu's conservatism is matched only by the kitchen's diligence. Simple dishes are cooked with the best ingredients and with absolute care. Warm Lyons sausage is served with potato salad, the house terrine is commendable, the salted herrings are deliciously oily, the brochette of mussels and petit sale with saffron rice is great stuff. Whiting is offered as a main course. Cheeses and wines are excellent.

L AND D MON TO SAT £70

FUNG SHING   4

15 Lisle St, London WC2 (020) 7437 1539
Variable Cantonese cooking. Deep-fried pig intestines, a sort
of red hosepipe, are pretty good. The hotpot dishes tend to
be crudely spiced. Decor is aspirantly European and prices
are slightly higher than is the Soho norm.

L AND D EVERY DAY £34

THE GARRICK CLUB   4

15 Garrick St, London WC2 (020) 7379 6478
Ouch! What was that? That was the rapier thrust of world-
class repartee. A mecca for witty barristers, modest journalists,
thoughtful politicians, humble actors. Expect first-class
theatrical paintings, first-class forelock, first-class Forte-style
cooking. Reciprocal membership with Stringfellows.

L AND D MON TO FRI £70

INCOGNICO   10

117 Shaftesbury Ave, London WC2 (020) 7836 8866
The name might make you wince and squirm, but this place
is up to scratch and then some. Nico Ladenis eschews novelty
and pursues excellence. The cooking possesses an apparent
simplicity that should fool no one: it takes 10 minutes and 30
years to cook a wing of skate to this degree of perfection. The
menu is long and offers nothing that you haven't seen before.
The point is: have you TASTED it before?

L AND D MON TO SAT £85+ (SET LUNCH £40+)

THE IVY   6

1 West St, London WC2 (020) 7836 4751
In the middle of the century this was among London's most
fashionable restaurants. It has been refurbished in a generically
1930s style which shuns pastiche. The atmosphere is sedate,
almost staid, certainly restful. The menu nods toward old-fashioned London 'continental' establishments, but the cooking is
vastly more accomplished. Smooth service. Impossible to book.

L AND D EVERY DAY £110

J. SHEEKEY   8

28-32 St Martins Ct, London WC2 (020) 7240 2565
A fine transformation of a once-grubby English fish restaurant.
It still looks like a long-established outfit. There are some
flights of fantasy on the menu, but it is the retro collations
that are the point: pickled herrings, rollmops with carrots and
onions and potato salad, near-perfect fritto misto, Dover sole
with brown butter, shrimps and soft herring roes.

L AND D EVERY DAY £110+

MON PLAISIR

5

21 Monmouth St, London WC2 (020) 7836 7243

Long-established bistro whose cooking is simple, balanced,
gloriously uninventive – mostly. When the kitchen does try
a spot of cuisine it's not necessarily successful. Best stick to
things like snails in garlic butter, mussels, John Dory on
stewed fennel, tournedos with bone marrow. The place is
cramped but most congenially run.

L MON TO FRI, D MON TO SAT £70+

MR KONG

5

21 Lisle St, London WC2 (020) 7437 7341

Good quality Cantonese cooking in plain surroundings. Satay
eels with fegara pepper are sensational and the 'sandpot' dishes
(casseroles) are outstanding.

L AND D EVERY DAY £40

THE NEAL STREET RESTAURANT

8

26 Neal St, London WC2 (020) 7836 8368

Antonio Carluccio's restaurant is overpriced, smoothly run, enjoyable if you're not paying. Dishes are simple, delicious, and make
the best of good ingredients. Eel is roast with bay leaves – and
that's it. Polenta is lifted by copious amounts of butter and cheese.
Grilled venison is served with a gamey morel sauce. Pasta is
doused in creamy butter and has white truffle shaved over it.

L AND D MON TO SAT £140+

ORSO

5

27 Wellington St, London WC2 (020) 7240 5269

Fashionable basement done out to look like Milan or Turin
of the early 1950s. Most dishes are of Piedmontese or
Lombardian provenance: sweetbreads with shallots, chicken
with olives and tomatoes. It successfully combines rusticity
with refinement. The attention to detail is great. Service is
by male models. Interestingly enterprising Italian wines.

L AND D EVERY DAY £70+

LE PALAIS DU JARDIN,

1

136 Long Acre, London WC2 (020) 7379 5353

The most unreconstructedly French of London's
mega-restaurants. Watercress soup is acceptable. Chewy
tentacular squid comes on a 'bed', or lumpy sofa, of soi-disant
risotto composed of diced potato and sweetcorn i.e., not
risotto at all. Steak tartare was wretched – a load of mincer-
extruded meat with two halves of infant tomato, an undressed
load of rocket and a couple of blobs of chopped caper.

L AND D EVERY DAY £75

POONS

4 Leicester St, London WC2 (020) 7437 1528

5

Undecorated cafe which serves one of London's greatest dishes –
hotpot of eel, belly pork and garlic. Also worth the trip are the
wind-dried meats and sausages, and the sea bass.

L AND D EVERY DAY £30

PORTRAIT RESTAURANT

National Portrait Gallery, St Martin's Pl, London WC2
(020) 7312 2490

1

There's a fabulous panorama if you get the right table. Since
you're not going to get anything much beyond the panorama, go
for it. You pay for the view, I guess. Desiccated salt cod fishcake
is not much of a reason to go there. Smoked salmon was better. A
glass of trashy Gamay was marked up by about five times. Avoid.

L EVERY DAY, D THURS AND FRI £80

PROSPECT GRILL

4-6 Garrick St, London WC2 (020) 7379 0412

5

This restaurant is devoted to quality and devoid of pretension.
Meats and fowls from Portwine butchers in Earlham Street
help out no end. Beef fillet is fully flavoured and comes with
an almost jammy béarnaise. Chicken is of good quality, as is a
monstrously deep burger of ground beef.

L AND D MON TO SAT £60+

THE RIVER RESTAURANT

The Savoy, Strand, London WC2 (020) 7836 4343

2

A lavishly mirrored dining room where punters pay an arm and
an uncoordinated leg to dine and dance to the sounds of the
resident band. The decent pasta in a lasagne is let down by
undercooked sweetbreads. A flavourless steak is accompanied by
chips that are cooked beyond al dente. Roast goose is delivered
on a trolley: the lukewarm slices are thus tired, grey and limp.

L AND D EVERY DAY £110+

RULES

35 Maiden Lane, London WC2 (020) 7836 5314

2

A stronghold of anachronistic John Bullishness which confirms
the predominantly touristic clientele's prejudices about the
mediocrity of trad English cooking. The wine list includes
'wines from former colonies'. Oysters, steak and kidney pudding with a grey suet crust and a desiccated haddock souffle
are to be avoided. Quail pie and an improbable black pudding
tart are not bad. The rooms are like a DIY version of the Soane
Museum (which is high praise). No smoking.

L AND D EVERY DAY £85+

SIMPSONS-IN-THE-STRAND

1

100 Strand, London WC2 (020) 7836 9112

Meat for the non-metropolitan. An anachronistic London institution, which is no doubt useful if you happen to be studying the mores and movements of French and Japanese tourists. The better dishes are those untouched by the kitchen.

L AND D EVERY DAY £90+

SOFRA

7

36 Tavistock St, London WC2 (020) 7240 3972

Instead of thinking this is bloody marvellous Turkish food you are enjoined by the cool occidental decor to think that this is bloody marvellous food full stop. Lahma – the grandfather of pizza – is offered in its classic form: minced spiced lamb is baked on a thin crisp base somewhere between bread and pastry. There are falafels with crisp exteriors and fondant interiors; a startlingly fine salad of cold artichoke served in its broth with tubers and beans. The grilled meats are exemplary and the small-grain basmati rice is terrific. There are more Californian wines than there are Turkish – the eschewal of national colour and folksiness is welcome.

L AND D EVERY DAY £55+

WEST STREET

9

13-15 West St, London WC2 (020) 7010 8600

One wall of the first-floor restaurant in this multi-partite operation comprises a fascinating selection of wine bins. A Tunisian carignan from Familia Zarrouk merits scrutiny. Rowley Leigh and Lawrence Keogh are fairly conservative cooks. They reinvent rather than invent. Lunch was as good as I've eaten in Britain for a while. Scallops with squid ink are served with tiny capers and bitter red chicory. Veal is brined, beaten out, cut into strips, rolled with sage and cooked on skewers – this is a fabulous dish. Pineapple sorbet was spot-on.

L AND D EVERY DAY. £75+, SET MEALS £45+

SW1

THE AVENUE,

3

7 St James's St, London SW1 (020) 7321 2111

One of the consultants is David Mellor – but, no, it's not the cutler, patron of architects and upholder of arts-and-crafts standards. It's the former Minister of Lurve, the man with fingers in so many pies he's got more hands than he has had hot dinners with despots. The architect is Rick Mather, who is only rarely allowed to show how clever he is. The cooking is not incompetent, merely miserly portioned and over-salted.

L AND D EVERY DAY £80+

LE CAPRICE
Arlington House, Arlington St, London SW1
(020) 7629 2239

A canteen for the more or less famous, which has the nous to treat everyone well. It does not fall into the trap of becoming an unofficial club. The staff is one of the best-drilled in town. Though the middlebrow classics (Caesar salad, eggs Benedict, smoked salmon with scrambled eggs) remain on the menu, the real interest is dishes such as rabbit with rosemary, risotto nero, chargrilled John Dory, etc. The attention to detail is total.

L AND D EVERY DAY £100+

CHRISTOPHER'S
Thistle Victoria, Buckingham Palace Rd, London SW1
(020) 7976 5522

To assert that this is far and away the best of London's railway terminus restaurants sounds like faint praise. It is not thus intended. This is a grand room – high and light and stately. But for all its pomp and elegance, it is host to a floating population of dazed transients, bodies killing time between cancelled trains. The food is designed to please the customer rather than to serve as a vehicle for the chef's self-advertisement. Recommended: spiced chowder of clams and cockles; grilled lobster; grilled Dover sole.

L AND D EVERY DAY £75

DRONES
1 Pont St, London SW1 (020) 7259 6166

Many of the customers give the impression of having rarely strayed outside SW1, SW3 and SW7. This is not a place to come to listen to estuarial accents. Posh is spoke. The long, low walls are hung with wallpaper that looks like veneer. There are dozens of framed photographs of Fifties and Sixties film stars. The cooking is delightful. Particularly recommended: an onion soup made with cider; a game terrine; cabbages stuffed with a coarse farce of liver and pork; oeufs à la neige.

L AND D EVERY DAY £120

EBURY WINE BAR
139 Ebury St, London SW1 (020) 7730 5447

Long-established outfit which is now predominantly a restaurant. The cooking is classy: boiled duck with vegetables; deep-fried squid 'chips'; chilli-infused crab cakes; a wonderful cep and potato soup; rare seared salmon with potato puree. The place is cramped, dark and, even though it has been comprehensively redecorated, it still retains a whiff of *The Crust On Its Uppers*.

L MON TO SAT, D EVERY DAY £60

THE FIFTH FLOOR   3
Harvey Nichols, Knightsbridge, London SW1
(020) 7235 5250

More than an in-store restaurant, although how much more
is moot. The kitchen is nothing if not eclectic: Madrid-style
tripe (iffy); bruschetta (ditto); fine Lancashire black pudding;
a quasi-Thai rendition of crab (first-rate); Franco-Italian
rabbit with lentils and mustard dressing (again, first-rate).
Commendable vegetables. Sumptuous wines include
deeply obscure bottles from such regions as Moldavia.

L EVERY DAY, D MON TO SAT £90+

FOLIAGE   6
Mandarin Oriental Hyde Park Hotel, London SW1
(020) 7201 3723

The restaurant is decorated according to its name. Although
each table has a little vase of flowers in a urine sample, the
theme is leaves. The chef is constantly over the top, but
he does over-the-top pretty well. A raviolo of chicken and
sweatbreads (sic) was first-rate. Lamb was impressive. Sea bass
was steamed and really excellent. The service is unflaggingly
courteous and tactful.

L MON TO FRI, D MON TO SAT £120, SET LUNCH £85

LA FONTANA   6
101 Pimlico Rd, London SW1 (020) 7730 6630

By no means standard-issue Italian corridor of a restaurant
which makes worthwhile attempts to break the mould. It
makes a big thing of autumnal fungus and is gifted at shaving
white truffle onto risotto. Excellent pasta with rarely
encountered sauces.

L AND D EVERY DAY £70+

THE GORING   6
15 Beeston Pl, London SW1 (020) 7396 9000

The interior makes it clear that this is a hotel which may love
a lord, but doesn't love a lord nearly as much as it loves a
king or a queen. The Royal Family has been here. Cocktails
are properly made, as are the endless stream of canapés. Eat:
poached sole with poached oysters in champagne sauce;
superb, almost meaty gravlax. Drink: this is a spectacularly
long list, 800 bins, which someone has felt obliged to annotate
with maximum banality.

L SUN TO FRI, D EVERY DAY. £125+

HUNAN   2
51 Pimlico Rd, London SW1 (020) 7730 5712

It claims, inaccurately, to be the only Hunanese restaurant in
London though the generic Chinese dishes tend to be better
than the Hunanese specialities.

L AND D MON TO SAT £70

L'INCONTRO   4
87 Pimlico Rd, London SW1 (020) 7730 6327

Superlative pasta at superlative prices. Apart from that,
the cooking is run of the mill.

L MON TO FRI, D EVERY DAY £130

ISOLA   5
145 Knightsbridge, London SW1 (020) 7838 1044

The ground-floor restaurant of this two-tier operation is more
exposed to the street than just about any other in London – did
anyone think about the gaping, resentful eyes of the bus queue
outside? It is based on the 1958 Chevrolet Corvette, an
absolute hymn to carmine, cream and chrome. A risotto of
porcini would have been better without the chicory; papardelle
al lepre lacked any specific hare flavour; bollito misto was
flawed. The pick of the lunch was hake poached in milk and
given a sauce of squid ink and red wine to signal effect.

L AND D EVERY DAY £130

LANESBOROUGH HOTEL, DINING ROOM   5
1 Lanesborough Pl, London SW1 (020) 7259 5599

Preposterously misjudged hotel – all repro furniture and
overbearing staff. The prices are outrageous – the wine
mark-ups are among the stiffest in town. The cooking is
self-consciously English, the menu prose is embarrassing, the
presentation of the food is nouvelle cuisine-ish. A lot of the
ancient and diligently researched recipes prove not to have
been worth exhuming. The pigeon pie is OK. Tea-flavoured
blancmange is pleasing and so is bread and butter pudding.

L AND D EVERY DAY £140+

MONTE'S   3
164 Sloane St, London SW1 (020) 7245 0896

Club for the orthodoxly rich, who are presumed to have no taste
save for orthodox luxuries – expensive wines, expensive food,
expensive eaux de vie, expensive cigars, expensive young women.
The money behind the outfit comes from Dubai. The manager is
'a relation by marriage of the Queen'. Quite a bit of the cooking
is off-target: a rather unpleasant juniper sauce with under-hung
venison; soapy-tasting cannelloni; a piddling portion of overcooked
pasta with seafood. On the credit side: a wonderfully flavoursome

fish soup; langoustine tails with white 'coco' beans; all the puddings and the peak-condition cheeses. Too much of the food betrays a pattisier's fussy hand.

L AND D MON TO SAT £150. MEMBERSHIP £500; JOINING FEE £250

Mr Chow

151 Knightsbridge, London SW1 (020) 7589 7347

A period piece. This was the first 'upmarket' Chinese restaurant and to some extent apes the trattorie of its period, the late 1960s. The food is merely a step up from a provincial chop suey house of the early 1960s. The place relies upon ignorant Knightsbridge hotel guests who don't know that they could eat four times as well for a quarter of the price in Soho. The prices are daring.

L AND D EVERY DAY £100

Nahm

The Halkin Hotel, 5 Halkin St, London SW1
(020) 7333 1234

A place not to visit at any cost – cost is a reason, though hardly the top one. The Australian chef, David Thompson, possesses genuine talents – for self-promotion, for reputation management. His cooking is all legerdemain, technical flashiness for its own sake. Most of the dishes taste of chilli, which is used with coarse abandon.

L MON TO FRI, D EVERY DAY £170

Noura

16 Hobart Pl, London SW1 (020) 7235 9444

This establishment does what restaurants are meant to do but which, in London, increasingly seldom do: it looks after its customers with unforced civility. It offers a menu of diligently prepared dishes based on proper ingredients. It's also the first London Lebanese restaurant which makes sense of the proposition that Lebanese cuisine is the best in the near Middle East. There is an estimable wine list with a number of Lebanese wines.

B, L AND D EVERY DAY £65

Olivo

21 Ecclestone St, London SW1 (020) 7730 2505

Proficient 'new wave' Italian cooking. Nothing fails, nothing shines. These are pretty good: stuffed squid dressed with tomato pulp; asparagus risotto; spaghetti with dried mullet roe.

L MON TO FRI, D EVERY DAY £100

ONE-O-ONE   6
Sheraton Park Tower Hotel, William St, London SW1
(020) 7235 8050
The restaurant has an air of desperation but the cooking is
delightful. Skate with balsamic vinegar, pancetta and sauté potatoes; a scallop and cep risotto; fillets of grey and red mullet with
couscous were all accompished, expertly realised plate-scrapers.

L AND D EVERY DAY £85+, SET LUNCH £65

L'ORANGER   3
5 St James's St, London SW1 (020) 7839 3774
Scumbling, banquettes, flowers, the titular orange tree, chairs
from a couture salon in Fifties Mayfair. Truffle oil is used with
abandon and with no sense that it might be the fashionable
bully of today: it overpowers a game terrine and a raviolo of
duck confit. Raw tuna is similarly swamped by a cross-cultural
cock-up of sesame oil and balsamic vinegar. Rabbit is spoiled
by an over-acidulated sauce. The staff are sweet-natured, naive
and convinced of the punters' ignorance.

L MON TO FRI, D MON TO SAT £90

PETRUS   9
33 St James's St, London SW1 (020) 7930 4272
Marcus Wareing has turned from being an also-ran into a
winner. His kitchen possesses a phenomenal deftness and a
wonderful lightness of touch. The balance between delicacy
and robustness is maintained on a knife edge. Roast foie gras
is served very hot indeed; it was sauced with a reduction of
Banyuls. A roast sweetbread was sauced with a Madeira and
truffle mix of improbable delicacy. Bass was roasted with
poached oysters and an oyster sauce. The cheeses are splendid
and there is a first-rate patissier on the team. The eponymous
bevvy is available in several vintages.

L MON TO FRI, D MON TO SAT £120, SET LUNCH £70

POMEGRANATES   7
94 Grosvenor Rd, London SW1 (020) 7828 6560
Publike, clublike one-off, run for more than a quarter of a
century by the eccentric and energetic Patrick Gwyne Jones,
who belongs to an almost vanished tradition of larger-than-
life hosts. The drawback to the basement dining rooms is
that they are frequented by politicians. Otherwise the place
is highly enjoyable, not least because it has adamantly neglected to keep up with the times – which of course means
that much of its menu now seems positively fashionable.
This is where gravlax was introduced to London and the
cure is good, even if the sauce is inauthentically sweet.
Although the menu is cosmopolitan, the most exotic and
unusual items are British: steak and kidney pie, boiled

chicken with parsley sauce and, best of the lot, salted
duck with an onion sauce.

L MON TO FRI, D MON TO SAT £75

QUAGLINO'S

6

16 Bury St, St James's, London SW1 (020) 7930 6767
A triumph of hype and, astonishingly, a triumph of large-scale
restauration. At every lunch and dinner more than 300 of Sir
Terence Conran's most intimate friends sit down to scoff
cooking of a quality that defies all expectation in a place of
such size. Vast portions of food which may be 'rustic' but
never crude: fresh cod with Jerusalem and globe artichoke
puree; a terrific pseudo-Japanese crab dish; a pudding called
Sauternes custard. There are dubious touches: a yob doorman;
the attempt to get punters to buy the ashtrays rather than let
them liberate them; the anachronistic cigarette girls; the
sometimes insolent staff. But, nonetheless, it's a hangar to
celebrate, and to celebrate in.

L AND D EVERY DAY £80+

RHODES IN THE SQUARE

9

Dolphin Sq, London SW1 (020) 7798 6767
Gary the Lad, the gelled telly supergeezer, is now so close to
being a tabloid icon it is all too easy to forget that, unlike the
other telly chefs, he really can cook. He brings French technique and imagination to bear on English staples. Take faggots,
for instance: the version done here uses finely chopped pigeon
meat; it is light, gamey and not dissimilar to a hot pâté. Lobster
thermidor omelette is some sort of culinary masterpiece. Mullet
is beautifully done in what is effectively a mullet soup.

L TUE TO FRI, D TUE TO SAT £110

SALLOO'S

7

62-64 Kinnerton St, London SW1 (020) 7235 4444
Offshoot of a successful restaurant in Lahore, this is a notable
address for carnivores. Although such things as dhal are first-
rate, the point of the short menu is meat. Lamb chops, lamb's
brains, chicken in batter; there's even wafer-thin meat in the
nan bread. The lassi is delicious. Prices are high, but worth it
for cooking of quite exceptional quality. If the service is slow it
is because dishes are cooked to order.

L AND D MON TO SAT £90

SHEPHERD'S

6

Marsham Court, Marsham St, London SW1
(020) 7834 9552
Westminster's unofficial canteen, which may be a treasonable
force of conservatism. The décor (gilding, carpets, mirrors,

booths) is far from cutting edge; the paintings are mostly of the
first half of the 20th century, mostly representational. Cooking
is old-fashioned – most of the dishes are English. Jellied eels
were done well, as was asparagus with a butter sauce. Venison
was marinated then grilled, and served with a delicious juniper
sauce.

L AND D MON TO FRI. £100.

VONG   3
Berkeley Hotel, Wilton Pl, London SW1 (020) 7235 1010
Hugely hyped and very glossy. Alsacien chef J-G Vongerichten's
gimmick is an effortully wrought synthesis of European and
South-East Asian ingredients and flavours. The results are showy,
patchy, pretentious. Spicing is timid and the prices are outrageous. The place is spatially impressive, decoratively inane.

L AND D EVERY DAY £120+

WILTON'S   5
55 Jermyn St, London SW1 (020) 7629 9955
Admirably straightforward British cooking – unostentatious
fish dishes and terrific savouries are among the things that
make this a one-off among the few worthwhile native
restaurants in London. The service is so good it wraps you in
a swaddling cloth of beneficence.

L AND D SUN TO FRI £110

ZAFFERANO   7
16 Lowndes St, London SW1 (020) 7235 5800
Cramped and not entirely elegant pair of dining rooms serving
some of London's better Italian cooking. Cabbage is stuffed
with pork and comes with a delicate meaty sauce. Pig's liver,
rarely found in restaurants, is done with borlotti beans and
button onions. Orecchiette are sauced with tomato and
chopped spicy sausages.

L AND D EVERY DAY £100

ZANDER   2
45 Buckingham Gate, London SW1 (020) 7379 9797
A Julyan Wickham tour de force in an art nouveauish building.
Shame about the restaurant which occupies it. The staff were
bored, gauche, hostile. Cooking was ham-fisted – imprecision
was the norm. The exceptions were a really good Spanish
omelette and the excellent bread. Garlic chicken was innocent
of garlic and innocent, indeed, of any flavour. 'Braised' lamb
was on a par with school cooking of 35 years ago.

L SUN TO FRI, D EVERY DAY £80+

City

1 LOMBARD STREET

1

1 Lombard St, London EC3 (020) 7929 6611

This inept restaurant occupies part of a typically overblown Edwardian bank beside the Mansion House. The decor is wildly subfusc. A clear vegetable broth was underflavoured. Salade niçoise was ghastly; tuna steak tasted of little; lamb shoulder was carelessly overdone. The mid-eighties acronym, LOMBARD, Loads Of Money But A Real Dickhead, could usefully be revived to describe the sort of person who patronises this joint.

L AND D MON TO FRI £100

ALBA

6

107 Whitecross St, London EC1 (020) 7588 1798

Piedmont-under-Barbican. A fair reproduction of a bourgeois Torinese restaurant; and you eat the way you might in that city. Vegetables are served as separate courses. Thinly sliced tongue is dressed with salsa verde. Gnocchi verde are sauced with gorgonzola. It's all plain in the proper way.

L AND D MON TO FRI £80

ARKANSAS CAFE

7

Unit 12, Spitalfields Mkt, Commercial St, London E1
(020) 7377 6999

The owner-chef and all-purpose character Kier 'Bubba' Helberg caters the American Embassy's Independence Day parties. He barbecues first-rate meat, most of it imported from the US, on grills that are like armoured cars designed by Heath Robinson. Choose from various cuts of beef, duck breasts and superlative burgers. Coleslaw makes one realise the point of that much abused salad. Cheesecake is unusually delicious. Drink beer or French cider.

L SUN TO FRI £40+

AURORA, GREAT EASTERN HOTEL

4

40 Liverpool St, London EC2 (020) 7618 5000

This restaurant breaks new ground for Sir Terence Conran by being dull. The hotel is a red brick intruder among the stone of the city. Its dining room is deep within the building and its only natural light source is a large domed ceiling lantern. That's the good bit. The rest is both vast and mean. Its entrance is meagrely proportioned; its colour scheme is insipid. A veal dish was preposterous. There was muscle meat, there was mushroom, there was mash, there was pasta – why? – there was cabbage, there was tripe. Everything was so denatured it had no flavour.

L SUN TO FRI, D MON TO SAT £125+

BRASSERIE ROCQUE

2

37 Broadgate Circle, Broadgate, London EC2
(020) 7638 7919
A well-run outfit, useful as a boozer, not so clever as a
restaurant; the kitchen is far too reliant on catering industry
short cuts and standardised pre-preparation. Some tables
outdoors.

L MON TO FRI £75+

LE CAFÉ DU MARCHÉ

4

22 Charterhouse Sq, London EC1 (020) 7608 1609
Congenial bistro frequented by carnivore surgeons from Barts.
Raw beef and steak are fine, the more elaborate dishes a bit of
a let down. Good sweets.

L MON TO FRI, D MON TO SAT £65+

CAFE SPICE NAMASTE

2

16 Prescot St, London E1 (020) 7488 9242
On the fringe of the City and very busy at lunchtime. The
interior is a riot of late-Eighties stencilling, scrap baroque and
all-purpose 'ethnicity'. The sub-continental menu is far from
standard issue and has a bias toward Goa. The kitchen aims
high, but is under such pressure that dishes tend to fail
through lack of attention. Chicken with piri-piri, a dish of
Portuguese/Goan derivation, is good and the peripheral items,
such as chutneys and relishes, show what the kitchen
is capable of.

L MON TO FRI, D MON TO SAT £60

CARAVAGGIO

7

107–112 Leadenhall St, London EC3 (020) 7626 6206
Reminiscent of Harry's Bar in Mayfair, but at half the price.
Carpaccio is served with rocket and a nicely oily pesto; mixed
cold seafood is good in an unshowy way. The pick of the
antipasti is a 'pâté' of chicken livers, which is nothing more
than a puree flavoured with truffle oil. Pasta is of a high order.

L AND D MON TO FRI £80+

CITY RHODES

9

New Street Sq, London EC4 (020) 7583 1313
Gary Rhodes may be some sort of hyperlad on the telly, but in
the kitchen he is double magic. His inventory of top-notch
dishes is long: cep and ham soup with a julienne of tarry
smoked meat; seared scallops with a carnal mustardy
bordelaise; and to finish, Jaffa cake pudding. The premises in
a Sixties block are smoothly modern.

L AND D MON TO FRI £100+

Club Gascon   9

57 West Smithfield, London EC1 (020) 7796 0600

Pascal Aussignac is a man with a mission to put this city on a diet of foie gras, duck, more duck plus duck fat. Recommended: grilled foie gras with toast and hot onion chutney; raw duck breast dressed with parsley; garbure; duck confit; celeriac puree with scallops; cassoulet. The chips are cooked in duck fat, as the best chips are.

L MON TO FRI, D MON TO SAT £50+

Coq d'Argent   4

1 Poultry, London EC2 (020) 7395 5000

The dining room is curved and tightly packed, comfortable, veneered. There is nothing wrong with the cooking – it is pleasingly unambitious and often reasonably proficient – but strenuous portion control and overpricing suggest it has been got at by accountants. Among the better dishes were: a chicken liver parfait; fried foie gras with nicely sauced lentils; a well-seasoned and properly timed veal chop. The garden could come to rival Clifton Bridge as a top topping spot. To Conran: to throw yourself from a high building after receiving a hefty bill.

L AND D MON TO FRI £95

THE Eagle   3

159 Farringdon Rd, London EC1 (020) 7837 1353

A one-off pub which owes more to Amsterdam cafes than to English tradition. It's noisy, chaotic and more than a tad like some arts lab. But the Italianate cooking is good despite some rough edges and the prices are low. There are well flavoured salads, marinaded steaks, mutton chops with tapenade and mash, and pungent soups. The portions are massive and only the ravenous could possible manage three courses.

L AND D MON TO FRI (NO BOOKING) £16–40

Eyre Brothers   3

70 Leonard St, London EC2 (020) 7613 5346

David Eyre, one of the founders of the Eagle in Farringdon, has moved on to a fully fledged restaurant, a handsome refurbishment of a Shoreditch warehouse or showroom. The interior is long, dark, lugubriously lit. Each of the ergonomically inept chairs cost £375. While the surrounds announce themselves as elegant, there has been no commensurate elevation of Eyre's cooking. The flaws of seasoning and timing that can be overlooked in a pub are less forgivable in an establishment charging grown-up prices.

L AND D MON TO SAT £100.

GAUDI RESTAURANTE

4

63 Clerkenwell Rd, London EC1 (020) 7608 3220
Eurocooking with Spanish inflections. Gazpacho is
overelaborated to the point where the name is meaningless,
but turbot was a lovely bit of fish.

L AND D MON TO FRI £80+

GEORGE

1

The Great Eastern Hotel, Liverpool St, London EC2
(020) 7618 7300
Sir Terence Conran's first pub comprises two rooms. The first
is a bar with wall-to-wall people yelling at each other; the
second a comfortable mustard-coloured dining room that seats
about 35 people. The cooking is pub grub. Some of it is pub
grub from before the advent of gastropubs. Steak and kidney
pie, for instance, is one of those little jobs in a bowl with a
pastry hat added. Plaice was overcooked in thick, greasy
retro-batter. Each chip was the size of a Mars bar. For reasons
that are hard to fathom, there are no real ales, only a meagre
selection of bottled beers.

L AND D EVERY DAY £65+

IMPERIAL CITY

5

Royal Exchange, Cornhill, London EC3 (020) 7626 3437
In the vaulted cellars of this city landmark is an unusual
Chinese restaurant whose menu has been 'devised' by telly
chef, Ken Hom. Much of the cooking comes from the Chinese
domestic repertoire – it is so unlike Chinese restaurant
cooking that one would be hard pressed to identify it were it
presented in a different way. The results are mostly pretty
impressive: belly pork braised with rice wine; salmon with
black bean paste; prawns in chilli sauce; orange pudding.

L AND D MON TO FRI £60+

MAISON NOVELLI

9

29 Clerkenwell Green, London EC1 (020) 7251 6606
After a stint as Ginola's double, as a kitchen philosopher, and as
a professional Frenchman, Jean Christophe Novelli is once again
doing what he is best at – cooking. And he really is a cracking
cook. Duck's neck is stuffed with duck meat, pork, pistachio and
foie gras. Wonderfully savoury rough pâté comes with pickled
cucumber; venison pâté en croute is as fine a cold crust pie as
you'll taste in Britain. Downstairs is a misnamed brasserie that is
actually a bistro; the restaurant upstairs is a super-bistro.

L MON TO FRI, D MON TO SAT £70 (£110 UPSTAIRS)

Moro   8

34-36 Exmouth Market, London EC1 (020) 7833 8336
This restaurant's success has had a notable effect on Exmouth
Market. Formerly rundown, this street is now all bars,
bookshops, upscale tailors. The kitchen, meanwhile, has
acquired real polish. Speculative Moorish touches are now
little in evidence. Salt cod croquettes with a jammy tomato
sauce was just the job; poached chicken was nicely succulent;
quail baked in flat bread remains a real one-off.

L MON TO FRI, D MON TO SAT £90

Moshi Moshi Sushi   4

Unit 24, Liverpool Street Station, London EC2
(020) 7247 3227
You sit at a bar perched above platform 1 and dishes pass in
front of you on a conveyor belt. Miso soup and beer can be
ordered from staff who patrol behind the customers. But the
main point is, obviously, sushi tuna, mackerel, yellow tail,
salmon, octopus, eel, etc. It's hugely popular at lunchtimes.

11.30AM–9PM MON TO FRI £30

THE Peasant   5

240 St John St, London EC1 (020) 7336 7726
A hastily converted pub on the street which, more than any
other, encapsulates London. The interior is rough and
spacious. Cooking is predominantly southern Italian,
skilfully done, very savoury, vastly portioned, extremely cheap.
Characteristic dishes include: a soup of borlotti beans and
bread flavoured with anchovies; ricotta and spinach dumplings
of unusual lightness served in a pungent thin tomato broth;
sardine fillets cooked with potatoes, mint, chilli and saffron
– a truly harmonious combination of flavours. There are cheap
wines, Adnam's beer on draught and several bottled ales from
Belgium, Italian amari.

L MON TO FRI, D MON TO SAT £40+

Potemkin   2

144 Clerkenwell Rd, London EC1 (020) 7278 6661
Named, presumably, for Einstein's film – there are framed
photos of Russian sailors on the stairs – rather than for the
lover whom Catherine the Great used when she wasn't having
a horse lowered onto her. If you want to drink yourself to death
on vodka, this is the place to do it. And while you are suffering
this most pleasurable suicide you can nibble at delicious cured
herrings, good smoked eel and salmon, cold roast stuffed pork
– but stop there because the main courses are indifferent.

L MON TO FRI, D MON TO SAT £70

THE QUALITY CHOP HOUSE

7

94 Farringdon Rd, London EC1 (020) 7837 5093

Punters are obliged to share booths in this unreconstructed and uncomfortable Edwardian dining room. Jellied eels show what a fine dish this can be if properly made. The black pudding is French and delicious. Steak tartare is excellent. There's a fair selection of wines at ungrabby prices.

L SUN TO FRI, D EVERY DAY £70+

RUDLAND AND STUBBS

0

35 Greenhill Rents, Cowcross St, London EC1
(020) 7253 0148

Fishy nursery grub served in self-consciously scruffy surroundings where sawdust predominates. A loud and hearty clientele munch fishcakes and swig black velvet.

L MON TO FRI, D MON TO SAT £60

SEARCY'S

6

Level Two, Library Floor, The Barbican London EC2
(020) 7588 3008

Bogusly bucolic cooking: sophisticated dishes with cosmetic rusticity a mandatory extra. Kidneys, liver and sweetbreads feature regularly. The trouble is that dishes tend to be on one note. Lamb cutlets and thymus are served with a potato gratin and too many veg; veal kidney is served with turnip gratin and baby carrots; ox tongue with beetroot and 'shaved' horseradish is recommended. Good oatcakes with the cheeses. The views of a rectilinear lake and St Giles Cripplegate are pleasing.

L SUN TO FRI, D MON TO SAT AND PRE-THEATRE ONLY ON SUN £70

SMITHS OF SMITHFIELD, TOP FLOOR

3

67-77 Charterhouse St, London EC1 (020) 7236 6666

The restaurant occupies a penthouse added to a Venetian gothic building of the 1860s. It is an attractive, if rather austere, space. The decked terrace with its extensive and enjoyable views is a boon. If only the chef, John Torode, could replicate the quality he achieved at Mezzo in the Nineties. £24 seems a grotesque amount to pay for a 10oz sirloin steak even if it was 'sourced' from a rare breeds wallah called Gary in Glos. Chicken was well-flavoured and the lemony gravy properly judged. The wine list is long, catholic, entirely lacking in halves.

L SUN TO FRI, D EVERY DAY £110

St John   10
26 St John St, London EC1 (020) 7251 0848
The restaurant feels original and fresh and vaguely bohemian.
Fergus Henderson's repertoire includes many parts of the
animal to which the popular reaction is one of coarse
fastidiousness. Tripe is cooked with onions in milk, or with
beans and sausages; lamb testicles are fried in breadcrumbs
and served with a splendid green sauce. Roast (veal) bone
marrow comes with a perfectly judged parsley salad. Dishes
are copiously served and mercifully undecorated. One of
London's one-offs.

L MON TO FRI, D MON TO SAT £60+

Sweetings   6
39 Queen Victoria St, London EC4 (020) 7248 3062
Immutable piscine survivor, which packs in all sorts of City
people in a weirdly democratic way. The premises are
beautifully decrepit. Good ingredients are prepared with care
and lack of adornment: skate is done with total correctitude,
black butter and capers.

L MON TO FRI, D MON TO FRI, BAR FOOD ONLY £90

Tatsuso   2
32 Broadgate Circle, Broadgate, London EC2
(020) 7638 5863
The ground floor, which has no view of the arena at the centre
of Broadgate, houses a tepan yaki bar. In the basement is a
standard-issue Japanese restaurant – high prices, production-
line cooking, mean portions.

L AND D MON TO FRI £100

Terminus   3
Great Eastern Hotel, Liverpool St, London EC2
(020) 7618 5000
The interior is sleek, elegant, correct and is achieved with the
polish which one has come to expect of the Eupeptic Knight,
Conran. The cooking would be better were it done by someone
who has learnt not to tart up simple dishes. A first course of
herring fillets was spoiled by an indifferent vinaigrette. Steak
and chips were OK. Béarnaise sauce was commendable. A
warm onion confection, a sort of vinous chutney, was poor.

B, L AND D EVERY DAY £70+

TWENTY FOUR   1
Level 24, Tower 42, 25 Old Broad St, London EC2
(020) 7877 2424
Bring binoculars and your own sandwiches. The view is the
restaurant's strong point. It takes in about 270 degrees – the
kitchen gets in the way of the southwest. Duck was so
peppered that whatever other flavour it might have had was
buried; salmon tartar was so cold that its flavour was muted;
steak was accurately cooked but flavourless. The service
wobbles and arrives like London buses.

L AND D MON TO FRI £90+

EAST LONDON

LITTLE GEORGIA   5
2 Broadway Market, London E8 (020) 7249 9070
A spartan former pub in the Hackney backwoods. Walnut is
as common in Georgian cooking as it is in that of southwest
France. Pomegranate, too, occurs frequently. Spinach is used
in combination with coriander in a sort of omelette and in a
cooked salad. All these are deftly done. The carnal main
courses had tendencies towards the leaden. There are a
number of Georgian wines, which should please the curious.

L SUN, D TUE TO SAT £45+

LMNT   2
316 Queensbridge Road, London E8 (020) 7249 6727
From outside, this Twenties Hackney pub looks, presumably,
much the way it always has – that's to say: nothing special. But
open the door and you step into a world of extraordinary
pharaonic kitsch. This is Nefertiti's krazee kottage. The cooking
is a very mixed bag indeed. Scallops are indifferent; a veal cutlet
was drowned by a creamy sauce; lobster tart was wretched.

L AND D EVERY DAY £85

SHANGHAI   4
41 Kingsland High St, London E8 (020) 7254 2878
A charming and original restaurant which has taken over what
was a pie and mash diner. It has stuck with the tiled decoration,
fixed tables and booths, and built an extra dining room, roof-lit
through neo-Edwardian lanterns. Out of one kitchen there
drools a series of Japanese fast-food versions of 'Chinese'
standards – sweet-and-sour pork with egg-fried rice, flaccidly
stir-fried udon noodles – which are worth avoiding. Dim sum
from Kitchen Two are of a quite different order. The quality is
exceptional: satays of eel, chicken hearts and chicken livers;
steamed prawn, pork and radish dumplings; pork puffs.

L AND D EVERY DAY £30

TABLA 6
The Dockmaster's House, Hertsmere Rd, London E14
(020) 7345 0345

The only subcontinental decorations are some reticently beaded ceiling lights. Cooking is pretty good. Lamb with 'bitter gourd' wasn't bitter at all but a heavyweight stew of that meat and squash. Wild boar jungle curry – what a name! – was a similarly hefty braise of pig and twigs, which turned out to be lentil pods. The preprandial pickles are splendid. But the kitchen simply can't turn round tables at the speed required by the people who work nearby.

L MON TO FRI, D MON TO SAT £60+

LE TIGRE ET LE GRENOUILLE 5
261 Bethnal Green Rd, London E2 (020) 7729 0829

The only restaurant in Britain that offers horse. The owner is a lanky Frenchman who's keen to vouch for the provenance of his horsemeat: it comes from Normandy, from beasts who've been on the trotting circuit. The fillet is done with an uncloying red wine sauce. It is dense, rare and well-flavoured. The rest of the bistro-like repertoire is equally acceptable. The room is a hodgepotch of bits and pieces. No expense has been afforded, for which we must give thanks: you can, as they say, eat your gift horse without paying through its nostril.

D TUE TO SAT £50

LES TROIS GARCONS 1
1 Club Row, London E1 (020) 7613 1924

The extravagant interior is camp in a disturbing, sinister way. There are dead animals and glass everywhere: it recalls some Beardsleyesque bordello catering to God knows what unspeakable aberration. The kitchen aims high, achieves low. A filo 'brique' was not cooked through and its contents recalled a supermarket spring roll. Lamb was served nearly raw rather than pink; sea bass was fried to a pulp. The prices are absurd.

L MON TO FRI, D MON TO SAT £125

UBON 4
34 Westferry Circus, London E14 (020) 7719 7800

The dining room, simpler than most of Philippe Starck's restaurant interiors, is high enough to afford fine westerly views up river to the City and beyond. Sunsets from here are likely to be extravagant – which is just as well. The portions are tiny, the menu is long and confusing. What the kitchen excels in is sashimi, deep-frying, cocktails and obliging service.

L MON TO FRI, D MON TO SAT £160

WAPPING FOOD 3

Wapping Hydraulic Power Station, Wapping Wall, London E1 (020) 7680 2080

The hydraulic pumping station was built in the early 1890s, converted to electricity in the Fifties, closed in 1977, and became a restaurant last year. There is a fair bit of heavy-duty machinery, hoists, chains, lifting attractive in its simplicity: steamed langoustines; Spanish charcuterie; unusually fully flavoured and tender beef rib; punchily dressed green salad.

L EVERY DAY, D MON TO SAT £80 PLUS

LONDON NORTH

N1

CASALE FRANCO 2

134 Upper St, London N1 (020) 7226 8994

Former light industrial premises which have been done over with ad-hoc brio. The place is in a yard and not easy to find – look out for Vulture Videos on Upper St. There is no booking in the evenings – which causes queues for the pizzas, which are only served then. If you are determined to queue for a pizza, this is a place to do so, in north London anyway. The rest of the cooking is unremarkable. Decent cheap wines.

L SAT AND SUN, D TUE TO SUN £60

GRANITA 2

127 Upper St, London N1 (020) 7226 3222

Vaguely Italian, vaguely health-freakish, vaguely pleasurable. Within its straightened limits the cooking is mostly all right, but reliant on the probity of its ingredients, which tend not to have suffered culinary intercession save of the most basic kind. The dining room is elegant. Service and wines are up to scratch.

L WED TO SUN, D TUE TO SUN £60

HUONG VIET 1

12 Englefield Rd, London N1 (020) 7249 0877

A Vietnamese restaurant occupying a detached Twenties public bathhouse. National colour comes in the form of wooden blinds, framed photos, and Vietnamese pop songs. Cold rice pasta rolls filled with prawn, veg and fennel have a London Rubber Company look to them. Beef soup is murkily flavoured. Barbecued lamb is much more the ticket.

L AND D MON TO SAT £30

LOLA'S
6

359 Upper St, London N1 (020) 7359 1932

The room, approached up rough slate and ochre stairs, is
designed to affront straying minimalists. There is a bit of
everything: neo-Adelaide chairs, Hoffman chairs, peppermint
banquettes, and more besides. Risi e bisi, soupy pea risotto
was spoilt by a feeble stock and undercooked peas. A second
risotto of (presumably dried or frozen) morels and asparagus
was much more the ticket. A version of the bread-based salad
or 'soup' called panzanella was delicious. Better still – an eggy
soufflé'd pancake or blini with soured cream, 'London' smoked
salmon, salmon eggs. Pudding: ice cream made from Greek
yoghurt, with various berries and honey.

L AND D EVERY DAY £70

THE REAL GREEK
8

13-15 Hoxton Market (off Coronet St), London N1
(020) 7739 8212

The Real Greek is not really Greek at all. It is far too good to
be really, genuinely Greek. The cooking makes the standard
north London items look like the industrial imposters they are.
The taramasalata will make anyone think twice about eating
the usual grot. Salt cod fritters suggest the source of the dish
that Captain Birdseye has debased down the years. Finish with
lukumadhes, hot little choux buns filled with honey and glazed
with yet more honey. The place looks like a low-budget pub
conversion, which means that the prices are kept down.

L AND D MON TO SA £70+

SOULARD
4

113 Mortimer Rd, off Englefield Rd, London N1
(020) 7254 1314

Competent and friendly bistro on the borders of Islington and
Hackney. The cooking is at its best when avoiding the simplicity
normally associated with such establishments. On the other hand,
the vegetable dishes are outstanding. Decent wine list.

D TUE TO SAT £70+

TARTUF
4

88 Upper St, London N1 (020) 7288 0954

This restaurant specialises in the Alsatian tarte flambée, which
is akin to a very thin-based pizza. The base is hardly thicker
than a water biscuit, and is as fatless. They are first smeared
with fromage frais and then a variety of other ingredients –
mushrooms and lardons, or first-class munster and lardons.
The choucroute is also well made. Dessert: another tarte
flambée with banana and chocolate.

L AND D EVERY DAY £35

Viet-Hoa
3

70 Kingsland Rd, London N1 (020) 7729 8293

One of half a dozen Vietnamese restaurants within a minutes walk from each other. The Vietnamese dishes (which are outnumbered by Chinese ones) are impressively light and aromatic. Soups are based on decent stocks. Coriander features in just about everything, save a dish of satay with a nicely savoury sauce. Spring rolls include some sort of pounded root vegetable.

L AND D EVERY DAY £30

NW1

Ali Baba
3

32 Ivor Pl, off Gloucester Pl, London NW1
(020) 7723 5805

Behind a takeaway in a central London backwater. The place is basically Egyptian, though it does dishes from all over the Middle East. Some of them are notable versions of standard items: falafel and smoked aubergine puree could not be bettered. The couscous is a disappointment in comparison. Sweet service.

L AND D EVERY DAY £35

Belgo Noord
3

72 Chalk Farm Rd, London NW1 (020) 7267 0718

Mussels in a dozen different ways, chips with mayonnaise. The beers are the point of this place and the selection is not at all bad.

L AND D EVERY DAY £50+

Great Nepalese
3

48 Eversholt St, London NW1 (020) 7388 6737

Dreary-looking place near Euston Station. The cooking is of exceptional quality: barbecued lamb with garlic and coriander, dahl of black beans, dumplings, mango kulfi.

L AND D EVERY DAY £30+

JOHN BURTON-RACE 6
The Landmark Hotel, 222 Marylebone Rd, London NW1 (020) 7723 7800

John Burton-Race is the kind of chef who measures his worth in Michelin stars – which'll give you some idea of how out of date he is. The heftily plasterworked late-Victorian dining room is so dismal that one wonders if it is a subtle joke that has misfired. The cooking's paramount characteristic is that of extraordinary expense. Cod was well-enough timed, though unremarkably flavoured. Raspberry soufflé with a raspberry sorbet was of a far higher order. Staff outnumber the customers and patrol the room with purposeless energy.

L MON TO FRI, D MON TO SAT £200, SET LUNCH £85

THE LANSDOWNE 4
90 Gloucester Ave, London NW1 (020) 7483 0409

Converted pub serving commendable and cheap food. Italian pork sausages with French bottled peas and mash; well-made mushroom risotto; salad with lardons and duck.

L TUE TO SUN, D EVERY DAY £40

LEMONIA 5
89 Regent's Park Rd, London NW1 (020) 7586 7454

The most elegant Greek Cypriot restaurant in London and probably the largest, too. The cooking is more refined than the taverna norm – but sometimes that refinement comes close to insipidity. Nonetheless, most of the standard-issue items are reasonably well done. It's a congenial place with a good atmosphere. The multicourse meze is a real bargain.

L SUN TO FRI, D MON TO SAT £32+

ODETTE'S 6
130 Regents Park Rd London NW1 (020)75865486

An established neighbourhood restaurant. There are fine terrines with well-spiced chutneys. Courgettes are deep-fried in the Roman manner; mullet and salmon are served with couscous. Lamb's rump and balls are served with a splendid jus and lentils. The wines are serious and seriously priced.

L MON TO FRI, D MON TO SAT £100+

VEGIA ZENA 4
17 Princess Rd, London NW1 (020) 7483 0192

The owners are Genoese and delightful 18th-century prints of that great baroque port hang on the walls. The cooking also recalls the city – which is not one of Italy's gastronomically stellar. Pasta is high-quality gear and, unusually, is used to accompany meat entrees. Spaghettini is sauced with garlic, oil and seafood.

L AND D EVERY DAY £65 PLUS

NW3

BENIHANA
2

100 Avenue Rd, London NW3 (020) 7586 9508
Gimmicky pseudo-Japanese diner dreamed up with California
in mind, no doubt. The chefs cook in front of the customers,
thus guaranteeing a fine film of fat on clothes and faces.

L AND D EVERY DAY £70

BRADLEY'S
3

25 Winchester Rd, London NW3 (020) 7722 3457
Well-frequented place in a Swiss Cottage backstreet. The
kitchen is interested in rampant eclecticism. Prawns in batter
are served on sticky rice with pieces of apricot and a jammy
apricot sauce. An ad-hoc Caesar salad is pleasing enough. A
triple-decker sandwich of potato, lobster and scallop is all
right. Sometimes the execution is imprecise. The wines are
all from the New World. Puddings tend to oversweetness.

L SUN TO FRI, D EVERY DAY £70

CAFE FLO
1

205 Haverstock Hill, London NW3 (020) 7435 6744
Basic 'French' dishes; steak and passable chips, unseasoned
gigot with flageolet beans, goodish vichyssoise. Branches
everywhere.

L AND D EVERY DAY £40

CUCINA
7

45a South End Rd, London NW3 (020) 7435 7814
Probably the best cooking in Hampstead. The food is better
than the interior, which is all Bobby Sands-style rag-rolling,
uncomfortable banquettes, mannered chairs, tiny tables. The
menu is perplexingly eclectic: steak and kidney pudding, miso
soup, squid and potato salad. The execution is, however,
uniformly precise. The kitchen is, perhaps, overfond of cheese,
but beef rib and chips is impressive. Nice service, nice prices.

L EVERY DAY (NOT SUNDAY IN AUGUST) AND D MON TO SAT £50

ED'S EASY DINER
1

255 Finchley Rd, London NW3 (020) 7431 1958
The phone number gets it right. This is a pastiche of anywhere
in America in 1958 seen through the eyes of a video maker or
ad director. Chrome, plastic, Dion and Elvis. The burgers and
milkshakes are all right but, no doubt, it is the feel rather than
the food that is of interest. Ideal for 40-year-olds re-living their
fantasy childhood.

L AND D EVERY DAY £20

WAKABA
122a Finchley Rd, London NW3 (020) 7586 7960

5

The ne plus ultra of minimalist decor, John Pawson's interior looks like the unfinished canteen of a high-tech micro optics lab in Uppsala. Punters should be obliged to wear black. As it is, they wear north London leisure gear. As expensive Japanese restaurants go, it is not over-expensive and the fairly standard repertoire is done with brio. The inventive appetisers include deep-fried salmon skin, which is delicious.

D MON TO SAT £100

ZAMOYSKI
85b Fleet Rd, London NW3 (020) 7794 4792

4

Downstairs is a wine bar with a puny wine list and mittel-European cooking. Upstairs is a folksy restaurant that offers decent Polish cooking, including a pancake of apple with smoked salmon, outstanding latkas, coulbiac, lightly cured sausage.

D EVERY DAY £45

ZENW3
83 Hampstead High St, London NW3 (020) 7794 7863

4

Europeanised Chinese cooking – which is a description, not a deprecation. Very high prices and very tiny portions, those are minus points. The cooking is sometimes quite inventive and invariably well executed: bass with tangerine peel and soy, scallops with ginger, deep-fried pork crackling, raw salmon and scallops with an odd sauce of soy and English mustard.

L AND D EVERY DAY £70, MUCH MORE IF YOU DRINK; DOUBLE THAT IF YOU EAT LOBSTER

ELSEWHERE

L'AVENTURE
3 Blenheim Terrace, London NW8 (020) 7624 6232

5

Pretty, pseudo-rustic bistro serving polished, pseudo-rustic French 'regional' dishes: veal with morels and fine fresh noodles, salad of duck confit, and so on. Good sweets, well-kept cheeses, flirtatious service by talkative patronne.

L MON TO FRI, D MON TO SAT £70

BU SAN
43 Holloway Rd, London N7 (020) 7607 8264

6

The best Korean cooking in London. The dining room is non-posh. It shakes with lorries on the road outside. Recommended: raw beef done with sesame seeds and sesame oil, aubergine with soya paste, deep-fried squid, fried pumpkin. This is down-home cooking, well done.

L MON TO FRI, D EVERY DAY £40

LE CADRE   4
10 Priory Rd, London N8 (020) 8348 0606
Vigorously Francophile bistro in an otherwise poorly served
part of London. However, it's not just popular by default. Some
of the cooking hints at a standard above usual: lamb with sage
sauce, caramelised onion soup, etc. The service is slow, the
wines are diligently chosen.

L MON TO FRI, D MON TO SAT £60

CHEZ LILINE   2
101 Stroud Green Rd, London N4 (020) 7263 6550
Mauritian fish restaurant specialising in Indian Ocean
species such as vacqua, capitain, bourgeois and sacre chien,
whose names are perhaps their most interesting quality.
Vindaye, cold fish smothered in a very hot paste, may be
a relation of vindaloo. Non-Mauritian dishes, such as an
attempt at bouillabaisse, are indifferent.

L MON TO SAT, D EVERY DAY £50+

CZECH AND SLOVAK HOUSE   5
74 West End Lane, London NW6 (020) 7328 0131
Looks like a bed-sitter which has been turned into a
restaurant. Hefty food well-prepared and served at knock-down
prices: boiled beef with dumplings, roast duck with dumplings,
dumplings with apricot. Good Czech beer and fruit spirits.

L SAT AND SUN, D TUE TO SUN £38

DON PEPE   5
99 Frampton St, London NW8 (020) 7262 3834
Animated Galician tapas bar that is an unofficial club for local
Spaniards. The black puddings, mountain ham and tortilla are
all commendable.

L AND D MON TO SAT £45

GEETA   4
57-59 Willesden Lane, London NW6 (020) 7624 1713
Fine south Indian cafe which, though it is mainly vegetarian,
serves some pretty good meat dishes. Rice flour dumplings,
potato pancakes, potatoes cooked with cream and chilli, dhal,
fruit-flavoured lassis, Rasam soup, all these are recommended.

L AND D EVERY DAY £30

GOURMET GARDEN

4

59 Watford Way, London NW4 (020) 8202 9639

The attractions here are the hotpot dishes and the Singaporean specials. Pig's trotter is not a good bet, but other hotpots are quail and wind-dried bacon done with rice wine and belly pork with coriander and soy sauce. Dover sole with blachan (prawn and chilli paste) is first rate. Laksa soup is on the crude side.

L AND D WED TO MON £60

ISTANBUL ISKEMBECISI

4

9 Stoke Newington Rd, London N16 (020) 7254 7291

Pleasant and original Turkish restaurant which avoids some of the clichés of that nation's kitchen and instead offers such recondite delicacies as brains, lamb's head, two forms of tripe soup, lamb's feet, etc. There are also some good salads. Drink Turkish beer or wine. Good-natured service and friendly prices.

L AND D EVERY DAY £30

KASHI-NOKI

5

Jarvis International, 18 Lodge Rd, London NW8 (020) 7586 0911

Although it surprisingly fails in its cooking of such standards as tempura and teriyaki, this dreary dining room serves some very good food. The range of sushi is large and includes such items as flying-fish roe, which is more a treat for the eye than the tongue.

L AND D TUES TO SUN £100

LAURENT

6

428 Finchley Rd, London NW2 (020) 7794 3603

Admirable Tunisian outfit which serves nothing but excellent couscous. The grain is served with combinations of grilled lamb and merguez sausages and with first-class broth. To start with, the Tunisian brik à l'oeuf is delicious. Cheap and potent Moroccan wine.

L AND D EVERY DAY £50

LOCAL FRIENDS

2

28 North End Rd, NW11 (020) 8455 9288

Suburban dim sum restaurants are rare and this one in Golders Green is useful for north Londoners. The menu includes the porridgey breakfast staple called 'congee' with a variety of accompaniments such as sea bass or abalone. Chaah siu and dumplings are sound enough. Eels are of massive girth, Cheung fun are OK.

L AND D EVERY DAY £35

NAUTILUS   5
27-29 Fortune Green Rd, London NW6 (020) 7435 2532
Probably the best fish and chip restaurant in London (also
takeaway). Crisp, grease-free batter, generous portions.

L AND D MON TO SAT £24

RANI   6
7 Long Lane, London N3 (020) 8349 4386
One of the finest Indian vegetarian restaurants in London. It
is not so much the many unfamiliar dishes that impress as the
extreme delicacy of the spicing and the differentiated flavours.
The deep-fried bhajias are unusually fine, the chutneys are
quite unlike those habitually encountered.

L SUN, D EVERY DAY £45

ROYAL COUSCOUS HOUSE   1
316 Holloway Rd, London N7 (020) 7700 2188
Just the job, should you wish to eat couscous in a bodged
front room on Holloway Road. The salads – potato, tomato
and onion, mashed aubergines – are rather better than the
titular dish. Stewed lamb is bland and relies on a fiery,
stinging harissa sauce for flavour.

D EVERY DAY (NO LICENCE, NO CREDIT CARDS) £25

THE SALT HOUSE   1
63 Abbey Rd, London NW8 (020) 7328 6626
Battered cod and sweetbreads were just about OK, though
the latter were lazily trimmed and imperfectly blanched.
Chips were alright; a salad was nicely dressed. Charmless
and grudging service.

L AND D EVERY DAY £40+

SHISH   7
2-6 Station Parade, London NW2 (020) 8208 9290
A glass-walled sore thumb in redbrick Willesden. A long
serpentine bar winds its way beneath ventilation ducts and
between exposed concrete piloti. In one part of the exposed
kitchen there are covetable Zumex juicers, in a second a
middle-eastern bread oven, in a third a salad preparation
area, in a fourth a char-grill. The cooking is mostly first-rate.
A kofta kebab was well-herbed and well-spiced; a similar
mix provided the filling for a splendid dumpling. Halva ice
cream was remarkable.

L AND D EVERY DAY £45

SINGAPORE GARDEN
7

83 Fairfax Rd, London NW6 (020) 7328 5314

Ignore the Chinese dishes (which are in the majority) and
stick to the Singaporean specialities. The ingredients are high
quality and flavours are true, clear, fresh. Satay is cut in large
enough lumps not to dry out during cooking. Laksa includes
glass noodles, prawns and fine fishcakes, and is a meal in
itself. Beef rendang is excellent.

L AND D EVERY DAY £65

TBILISI
6

91 Holloway Rd, London N7 (020) 7607 2536

The decor comprises a carpet on a door, some Bayswater
Road School nocturnes of Tbilisi and a tourist poster. The
cooking is splendid, with the exception of a dish called Fish
Monastic – a trout, potato and cheese gratin. Otherwise there
is light, crisp, spongy bread filled with either cream cheese or
bean puree; fricassee of lamb's liver and heart; savoury meatballs in doughy pasta; lamb stew. Drink a Caucasus red
called Matrassa, which is as dry as parchment.

D EVERY DAY £40

THE TWO BROTHERS
6

297 Regents Park Rd, London N3 (020) 8346 0469

A London oddity – a truly vernacular place: people with
Rollers parked outside, scruffy young couples and smart
elderly ones, Japanese families, French families. This is a fish
and chip joint that is above fashion. The interior is large, all
wood. Service is civility itself. The cooking essays the commonplace and raises it to otherplace. Cod in batter is done by
cooks, not by hack fish-fryers; the chips are greaseless; lemon
sole is done on the bone in matzo meal. Arbroath Smokies are
done in a creamy gratin.

L AND D TUE TO SAT (BOOKINGS FOR LUNCH ONLY) £28

London South

SE1

BALTIC
6

74 Blackfriars Rd, London SE1 (020) 7928 1111

The menu is mostly Polish and the portions are on the vast side, but better that than meanness – you can always leave some. I left most of my chlodnik: I've liked this beetroot soup since I discovered Dacquise in my late teens. The version here lacked hard-boiled egg, was much too creamy and had a load of raw dill-like lawnmowings floating on it. Other than this, the cooking was pleasing. Predominantly female, predominantly Polish waitresses are cheerily efficient and the housedog, part Jack Russell (but without the temper), is delightful.

L AND D EVERY DAY £75, SET LUNCH £44

THE BLUEPRINT CAFE
9

The Design Museum, Butler's Wharf, London SE1 (020) 7378 7031

The great Jeremy Lee cooks with constant aplomb: belly pork with butter beans; duck breast sauced with soy and ginger. The river view is beguiling.

L EVERY DAY, D MON TO SAT £90

THE BUTLER'S WHARF CHOPHOUSE
3

36e Shad Thames, London SE1 (020) 7403 3403

Conran's attempt to rehabilitate English cooking the way that the Greenhouse has done is partially thwarted by the kitchen's laxity. Roast beef is flavourless, Yorkshire pudding is leathery. Some of the desserts, too, leave much to be desired. Best stick to (heavyweight) steak and kidney pudding and to grilled smoked eel and bacon with a potato pancake. The view of Tower Bridge is smashing; the clientele chappish, loud, City. Prices are insultingly high.

L EVERY DAY, D MON TO SAT £80+

CANTINA DEL PONTE
3

36c Shad Thames London SE1 (020)74035403

Conran Italian, and quite the loudest of the Peptic Tycoon's many outfits: people come here to yell. Service is so-so. The kitchen is similarly up and down. The Milanese risotto here is as good as you'll find in London; it is served with the strange and delightful accompaniment of whiting fillets. But there is also flavourless pork chop, with an unsuccessful mix of beans and mostarda di frutta, and an equally iffy tomato timbale. The wines aren't that special, but there are lots of brands of grappa.

L AND D EVERY DAY £70

CHAMPOR CHAMPOR   4
62 Weston St, London SE1 (020) 7403 4600
This is an outfit whose take on eastern cooking dispenses with
the rule book. It is tiny, inexpensive, entirely homemade (the
chef did the paintings). The kitchen turns out a bewildering
range of dishes of Malaysian, Thai, Sri Lankan and Japanese
provenance. Seared salmon with pearl barley and a soy and
chilli dip is delightfully delicate; buffalo salad had such an
excess of chilli it was almost inedible. Granitas are made
from chrysanthemum and hibiscus.

L TUES TO FRI, D MON TO SAT £45

THE CIRCLE   1
Queen Elizabeth St, London SE1 (020) 7407 1122
The circle is a Docklands development of the mid-Eighties
by CZWG that retains its power to startle, no matter how
frequently it is seen. The bar and restaurant that has taken its
name also tries to borrow its date. Cooking is a throw-back to
the dismal days of British 'nouvelle cuisine'. A 'walnut' salad
was bereft of those nuts. A consomme of mussels and leeks
was so flavourless it tasted of the spoon used to eat it; scallops
were done with capillaries of lemongrass teased to resemble a
beehive hairdo.

L AND D EVERY DAY £45+

THE FIRE STATION   4
Waterloo Rd, London SE1 (020) 7620 2226
A very good deal indeed. A vast space furnished from junk
shops with an open kitchen on one side and bar on the other.
The cooking has its rough edges, but most of it is done with
flair. Portions are massive and the atmosphere is good. The
place is packed, which means that latecomers often have to
choose from a restricted menu. Wines are cheap, Young's
bitter's better.

L AND D EVERY DAY £30+

FISH!   4
Cathedral St, London SE1 (020) 7234 3333
The building is a former hall of the Borough Market, a fine
bit of Victorian engineering which begins in a railway arch
and curves gently toward Southwark cathedral. The card lists
20 or so species of fish, which can be served with a choice of
sauce and ticks those which are available each day. Cooking
is admirably restrained: fine ingredients, perfect timing and
a total lack of kitchen exhibitionism. Recommended: devilled
whitebait; grilled lobster; battered fish; grilled squid. Loud
music.

L AND D EVERY DAY £65

THE HONEST CABBAGE 5
99 Bermondsey St, London SE1 (020) 7234 0080
A former pub done out with cream and sage-green paintwork,
hefty neat tables, ex-church chairs. The daily changing menu
offers a soup, a pie, a pasta, one meat dish, and so on. There are
flavoursome steaks, butch chips and cuts like veal chops. Prices
are so low they give you some idea of the con perpetrated on the
public by most of the restaurant trade. The coffee is potent;
the wines are cheap; the music can be irritating.

L EVERY DAY, D MON TO SAT £50

LIVEBAIT 3
43 The Cut, London SE1 (020) 7928 7211
Black-and-white tiled room which recalls Edwardian public
lavatories. Raw molluscs and crustaceans are straightforwardly
served, but the cooking aims for too much cuteness. Now
part of a chain.

L MON TO FRI, D MON TO SAT £70

MESON DON FELIPE 2
53 The Cut, London SE1 (020) 7928 3237
Pleasant tapas bar near Waterloo frequented by Marbella
hands. Meat dishes are better than fish ones. Good cheeses.

L AND D MON TO SAT £45

NEAT BRASSERIE 4
**2nd Floor, Oxo Tower Wharf, Bargehouse St,
London SE1** (020) 7928 4433
This restaurant is light, elegant, mauve, orange, pale copper
and misnamed – it is most certainly not a brasserie. The menu
suggests that Richard Neat has but a passing acquaintance
with brasseries and is locked into the milieu of haute cuisine.
A quail ballotine was a ballotine the way the brasserie is a
brasserie. Still, not bad. Both ox tongue and slow-cooked lamb
were indistinctly and similarly sauced. Old-fashioned desserts
are served on a trolley.

L AND D EVERY DAY. £80+

THE OXO TOWER BRASSERIE 2
Barge House St, London SE1 (020) 7803 3888
The Thamescape, stretching from the Shell Building and
the Savoy to the former Natwest tower and Lloyds, is hugely
impressive. The bills are at least 25 per cent higher than they
should be for perfectly reasonable but unmemorable cooking:
pumpkin risotto, onion tart, etc. Puddings are all right.

L AND D EVERY DAY £80

THE PEOPLE'S PALACE

1

Level 3, Royal Festival Hall, Belvedere Rd,
London SE1 (020)79289999

An effective job of turning the decorative clock back to 1951 has, unhappily, been complemented by the kitchen's essay in non-specific anachronism. The place is a litany of hedged bets: the service is grand hotel, the food is upmarket pub grub of the day before yesterday. River views make up for a bit of this.

L AND D EVERY DAY £65

LE PETIT ROBERT

2

3 Park St, London SE1 (020) 7357 7003

A throwback to the undemonstrative London bistro. The dining room is as tweely drab as a Laura Ashley dress, all algae-green gloom, plates on the wall, dried flowers, dull prints. But the chef can cook – cautiously, conservatively and generously. Duck livers, fried and sauced with cream and brandy, were bland. Wild boar in another cream sauce was well-made and more surely flavoured, although the meat itself was indistinguishable from pork.

L AND D MON TO SAT £60, SET LUNCH £30

PIZZERIA CASTELLO

3

20 Walworth Rd, London SE1 (020) 7703 2556

Big restaurant with ranks of pizza ovens by the door, utilitarian decor, fantastic bustle as though this was Naples itself. The prices are pretty reasonable. Drink Colle Secco. The pasta dishes are perfectly OK, but don't really match the main business of the place.

L MON TO FRI, D MON TO SAT £30

LE PONT DE LA TOUR

5

The Butler's Wharf Building, 36d Shad Thames,
London SE1 (020) 7403 8403

Smart warehouse conversion a couple of hundred yards southeast of Tower Bridge. Like all of Conran's enterprises, it has been undertaken with spirit. This time, though, it's more hit than miss. The cooking is a French dream of Britain. It tends toward heaviness but has sufficient oomph to see it through. Fish and chips is better than almost any chippie (it also costs more); salt pork with lentils is excellent. Vegetables are substantial – here is a kitchen that can braise cabbage and boil potatoes. The puddings don't meet the standard of what precedes them.

L AND D EVERY DAY £120+

RSJ   3
13a Coin St, London SE1 (020) 7928 4554
Almost certainly the most extensive selection of Loire wines
in Britain, and there can be few places in the Loire valley itself
which match it. The cooking has little affinity with these
wines. It is run-of-the-mill Franglais stuff. What should be
hearty, wintry dishes are spoiled by daintiness. Fish is rather
better dealt with.

L MON TO FRI, D MON TO SAT £55–£70

TAS   6
33 The Cut, London SE1 (020) 7928 2111
An improbable meld of ocakbasi restaurant and brasserie. There
is an open-grill kitchen, an air of energetic purpose, an epic
menu of standard-issue items, which are decently prepared and
copiously served. Hummus, tarama, aubergine puree, then a
crude but tasty fish stew, casseroled chicken and lamb's kidneys.

L AND D EVERY DAY £40

TENTAZIONI   7
2 Mill St, London SE1 (020) 7237 1100
An interloper in Conrania, which has the nerve to shun even
passable design, and has dared to offer cooking which surpasses
just about everything which calls itself Italian in London. Veal
carpaccio is served lukewarm with a similarly warm chutney-like
mix of chopped aubergines and dried tomato that was spiced
and perfumed. Tortellini are stuffed with pheasant paste and
sauced with pureed potato; rabbit navarin is fabulously savoury.

L TUE TO FRI, D MON TO SAT £60+

ELSEWHERE

ARANCIA   1
52 Southwark Park Rd, London SE16 (020) 7394 1751
The first problem is the music – drooling jazz, dismal rock –
which the waiting staff are reluctant to turn down. The food
isn't much good either. Pasta with an insipid, flavourless sauce
is not enhanced by the salt served in a grubby little bowl;
pheasant comes with watery mashed potatoes.

L WED TO SUN, D MON AND TUES £50

BABUR BRASSERIE   2
119 Brockley Rise, London SE23 (020) 8291 2400
The cooking is inventive rather than founded on a particular
region of the subcontinent. Minced lamb comes with an
industrial bap; duck with a fiery red sauce.

L SAT TO THURS, D EVERY DAY £45

BELAIR HOUSE
Gallery Rd, London SE21 (020) 8299 9788

7

A late 18th-century house in its own park in the middle of
Dulwich. Cooking is robust, done with precision and properly
seasoned. Puddings are top-notch.

L TUE TO SUN, D TUE TO SAT £90+

BRADY'S
513 Old York Rd, London SW18 (020) 8877 9599

4

An oddity: a fish and chip restaurant run by a restaurateur. It
thus avoids the usual hurdles of stench and customer abuse.
But, beyond this, it's estimable as a purveyor of well-battered
white fish, first-rate smoked salmon, decent puddings. Cheap
wines and beers.

D MON TO SAT (NO BOOKINGS, NO CREDIT CARDS) £34+

CAFE PORTUGAL
5a-6a Victoria House, South Lambeth Rd, London SW8
(020) 7587 1962

1

Two tiny rooms with a small bar on the ground floor of a
fortress-like tenement block. There are a few tokens of
national colour, a jolly proprietor, indifferent food. The kitchen
pulls off the impossible by creating something insipid from salt
cod: torpedo-shaped croquettes that taste of potato. These
were preferable to a warmed-over dish of pork, clams and
potato – tough meat, leathery tubers, mostly empty clam shells
and a bath of indeterminate oil.

L AND D EVERY DAY £40

CASTILLA
82 Battersea Rise, London SW11 (020) 7738 9597

1

A congenially gloomy tapas bar with dark pedimented shelves
loaded with rarely seen Spanish brandies and liquers. Tripe
and chickpeas come out of a tin – but better a moderately
competent dish out of a tin than a bad one which has been
homecooked. Tuna and pepper empanada is delicious, with
nicely done short pastry and a proper savoury filling. Potato
tortilla was insufficiently eggy, insufficiently seasoned.
Meatballs in tomato sauce were just the way Paulie made
them in the big house in *Goodfellas*.

D MON TO SAT £40+

CHEZ BRUCE

2 Bellevue Rd, London SW18 (020) 8672 0114

Bruce Poole is an Englishman whose Francophilia is total.
He is also a severally talented chef and has enough savvy to
throw in a few dishes which are not pastiches of provincial
France 30 years ago, but they're not the point. The following
are recommended: a butch pot au feu; roast cod with
gremolata and unctuous potato purée.

L EVERY DAY, D MON TO SAT £110+

DEL BUONGUSTAIO

283 Putney Bridge Rd, London SW15 (020) 8780 9361

A convincingly done replica of an early 20th-century restaurant
that you might find in the suburbs of Rome. Cooking veers toward
timidity. The pre-prandial plate of savouries is mostly all right.
Thereafter, potentially good dishes, such as eel stew or veal with
rocket, are marred by a fretful hand and insipidness. The puddings
are good.

L AND D EVERY DAY (SUN CLOSED IN AUGUST) £55

DEWANIAM TANDOORI RESTAURANT

133 Stanstead Rd, London SE23 (020) 8291 4778

Unusual Indian restaurant which serves hare, duck, venison, etc.
But it does not cook them especially well. Outstanding lassi.

L AND D EVERY DAY £40

ESTRELA

111–115 South Lambeth Rd, London SW8
(020) 7793 1051

An opportunity to inhabit Portugal on Thames for the price of a
drink: a TV is tuned into Lisbon's daytime schedule. More comfortable than a standard London pub, but the cooking isn't much
of an improvement on the dull pub norm. Portions are large,
dishes filling, flavours bland. Caldo verde was glutinous with
pureed potato and contained nothing to lend it flavour apart from
a tiny disc of chorizo. Feijoada, a belly pork and bean stew, is rich
and warming. Cheese, plastic and pre-sliced, is to be avoided.

L AND D EVERY DAY £25+

GASTRO

67 Venn St, London SW4 (020) 7627 0222

Scruffy, hippyish venture furnished from junk shops serving
unambitious but mostly competent bistro grub: fish soup with
rouille; good andouillette with sauted potatoes. These are
bought-in items. When the kitchen has to prepare, or, rather,
assemble ingredients, it is not clever – salad niçoise was inept.

BREAKFAST, L AND D EVERY DAY £30

GOURMET BURGER KITCHEN   3
44 Northcote Rd, London SW11 (020) 7228 3309

This place makes a real effort: organic meat, careful timing,
fresh pressed fruit juice – oh, and woefully cramped seating.
But forget that. It is not really a restaurant but a new breed of
diner devised for a clientele that shuns McDonald's and its
kin but enjoys the speed and convenience of such places.

L AND D EVERY DAY £30

HARVESTER: THE DUTCH HOUSE   0
Sidcup Bypass, London SE12 (020) 8857 4892

One of the many dispiriting aspects of Harvester – which has
about 130 branches – is the realisation that this is what the
bulk of the British population understands by a restaurant. The
food – an approximate word in the circumstances – leaves
one, left me, feeling sullied, bucally and peptically polluted.

L AND D EVERY DAY £45

KASTOORI   5
188 Upper Tooting Rd, London SW17 (020) 8767 7027

The cooking is Gujarati out of east Africa and is executed with
flair and spirit. It is entirely vegetarian and astonishingly rich.
The thali comprises standard-issue items of a level way above
standard – a mild dhal, an earthy lentil stew, a potato curry, a
mixed veg curry, deliciously light rice. Tomato curry is
thrillingly fresh tasting. The lassi is excellent and so is the lassi
milkshake.

L WED TO SUN, D EVERY DAY £40

THE LOBSTER POT   3
3 Kennington Lane, London SE11 (020) 7582 5556

The nautical/piscine restaurant is a type which refuses to
change with the years. Outside there is a lifesize cut-out of
the proprietor and beside it, on the pavement, a lobster pot.
Within there is a shriek of gulls and the rumble of Breton
shanties. There are also portholes, an aquarium, ropes and
nets, waiters in horizontally striped sailor tops... Fish soup was
fairly good. A mixed grill included tuna, lobster, squid, sardine,
clams, etc. and was OK, but the timing was imprecise and the
seasoning haphazard. The standard-issue seafood selection of
whelks, oysters, winkles, crab, and so on was the most
successful item.

L AND D TUES TO SAT £85

MA GOA

4

244 Upper Richmond Rd, London SW15 (020) 8780 1767

The only Goanese restaurant in London, and thus the only place to get a remotely correct vindaloo – a vinegary braise of belly pork thickened with nuts. Also worth trying are a herby green 'curry', shrimp masala, stuffed poppadom and the semolina-based pudding called sooti halwa.

D TUE TO SUN £50

MASALEDAR

3

121 Upper Tooting Rd, London SW17 (020) 8767 7676

A rarity among subcontinental restaurants in that it is owned by Muslims from Tanzania, who cook wearing slightly clownish headgear at a glass-baffled counter. Char-grilling is done rather literally – tiny, spiced lamb chops were arson victims, but pretty tasty. Ditto veg samosas, served with home-made chutney. Good lassi and fresh fruit juices (the premises are teetotal).

L AND D EVERY DAY £25

MCDONALD'S

1

56 Powis St, London SE18 (020) 8317 0102

Hospitals no longer minister to patients but to customers. Where did the patients go? To McDonald's, – jabbering crones, wobbling toddlers, squaddie-hunting schoolgirls, hard cases with bad tattoos. The chips aren't too bad, if you leave half of the carton. This was London's first branch of the unstoppable scent.

ALL DAY, EVERY DAY £8

NUMIDIE

7

48 Westow Hill, London SE19 (020) 8766 6166

Serge Ismail is a Marseillais Berber, whose unusually home-made restaurant is more French than it is north African. When it is north African, or Numidian, it is those in a French way. There's a gratinated brandade, there's steak with a smothering of foie gras and gratin dauphinois. Especially there are merguez with a child's tomato sauce of some force and a fish tagine. It's all enjoyable, proficiently prepared and served with unaffected charm.

D TUES TO SUN, L SUN £50

OSTERIA ANTICA BOLOGNA

5

23 Northcote Rd, London SW11 (020) 7978 4771

Cramped, studenty, all-wood outfit that serves a number of rare (and inexpensive) wines and a long, varied menu of recondite dishes: lamb cooked in milk, goat stewed with tomato, sardines with raisins and pine nuts. Despite the place's name, most of these dishes are of southern inspiration and demonstrate that there is more to that part of Italy than pasta with tomatoes.

L AND D EVERY DAY £50

LE P'TIT NORMAND

4

185 Merton Rd, London SW18 (020) 8871 0233

Fake beams abound, but the cooking is the real thing, arteriosclerotic Norman specialities in all their creamy splendour: veal, pork and shellfish all get roughly similar treatments. The few dishes that do not include cream are heavy with apples, cider and calvados. Norman cheeses are good and the wines are inexpensive.

L SUN TO FRI, D EVERY DAY £50

PUTNEY BRIDGE

6

Embankment, London SW15 (020) 8780 1811

An architectural delight: nautical, curvy, sleek and apt for a riverine setting. A pork terrine was a first-rate example of the charcutier's craft. Risotto Milanese was well-made; suckling pig particularly toothsome. Chips are fried in good dripping. The least likeable feature of the place is its prices.

L TUE TO SUN, D TUE TO SAT £110

RANSOME'S DOCK

7

35-37 Parkgate Rd, London SW11 (020) 7223 1611

Martin Lam's kitchen seems to have made a calculated (and welcome) decision to avoid the cutting edge. I guess you could call the cooking Franglais: but it's good. It's certainly more appealing than pan-Asian with a Levantine twist. Main courses are copiously portioned, precisely cooked: steak from a shorthorn with a red wine sauce and green beans; calf liver with bacon. Cheeses are of the highest quality.

L EVERY DAY, D MON TO SAT £85+

RIVA

9

169 Church Rd, Barnes, London SW13

(020) 8748 0434

It could have been airlifted from Lombardy. Andrea Riva has taken the trouble to cultivate one of Britain's several million coarse fishermen and asked him not to release the pike he catches; he serves it slightly warm with salsa verde. He also brings in shad from his native Como, salted, which he fries. Herrings are done with saor, the understated vinegary confection, and with raisins and pine nuts; gnocchi are sauced with meaty porcini; steak is first-class.

L SUN TO FRI, D EVERY DAY £85+

SELSDON PARK HOTEL

4

Addington Rd, Sanderstead, Croydon (020) 8657 8811

The hotel that gave it's name to Selsdon Man in 1970 and, indeed, there's an Edward Heath Suite. Also of that decade is the Phoenix Bar, which owns the looks of an Eastern European airport lounge. The hotel is barrack-like and has a conference centre and a golf course. The rather grim dining room has a pianist who knows his way round James Bond themes. Some of the food is predictably dire but a rich and properly gamey hare pie, an authentic osso bucco and a substantial dish of Toulouse sausages suggest that the kitchen can cook, if it wants to.

L AND D EVERY DAY £85+

SONNY'S   4
94 Church Rd, London SW13 (020) 8748 0393
Fashionable bistro-ish cooking, mostly well brought-off, although now and again inclined to cuteness. For instance: chicken with fried banana with a spice sauce; almost raw beef with pickled ginger. Simpler things, such as deep-fried lamb's brains, are a better bet. Good chips, good salads.

L EVERY DAY, D MON TO SAT £70+

STATION GRILL   3
2 Braganza St, London SE17 (020) 7735 4769
Once inside the locked door you might be anywhere. The street outside is obscured by frosted, etched glass. Dishes tend to be marred by misplaced accents and and cute affectations. Bavette was overdone while the sauce with it was 100 per cent Bovril. Rabbit saddle with noodles coated in garlic cream was above and beyond rich. Chocolate tart and fruit jelly were startlingly delicious.

D TUES TO SAT £30

THE STEPPING STONE   3
123 Queenstown Rd, London SW8 (020) 7622 0555
Smart, bright, colourful, angular. The interior is up-to-the-minute. The staff work hard and the place sweats good intentions, but the cooking's tendency toward unintegrated dishes precludes the exchange of flavours. Nothing seems more than the sum of its parts. And too many elementary mistakes are made: duck livers taste metallic because they have not been soaked in milk; a fried cake of Jerusalem artichoke is unseasoned. All peripheral items are properly attended to: the choice of beers and wines is amiable. Bread is well made; most of the puddings are up to scratch.

L SUN TO FRI, D MON TO SAT £70

THAILAND   4
15 Lewisham Way, London SE14 (020) 8691 4040
Much of the cooking in this cramped outfit is very hot indeed – it comes from the Thai/Laotian border. Excellent green curry and fish cakes.

L TUES TO FRI, D TUE TO SAT £50

West London

W2

L'Accento Italiano
4

16 Garway Rd, London W2 (020) 7243 2201

Classy, rustic Italian cooking. The premises are undecorated;
the atmosphere party-like. Recommended: tripe with borlotti
beans, pork fillet with agrodolce sauce, roast vegetables, oxtail
with tomato and celery, squid-ink risotto, fruit fritters. Good
service, cheapish wines.

L AND D EVERY DAY £55+

Al San Vincenzo
8

30 Connaught St, London W2 (020) 7262 9623

A self-taught Neapolitan chef whose repertoire is akin to that
of the better British chefs, albeit with a slight Italian accent.
Not an address for either pasta or polenta. But there is some
kinship with the nuova cucina chefs of Rome and Turin. Chef
Borgonzolo is very subtle, has an airy touch with apparently
rustic dishes. Rabbit with a sweet and sour sauce (which
makes one understand the point of that sauce) is good; risotti
are good; the wine list is good. It's altogether an oddity, and a
welcome one.

L MON TO FRI, D MON TO SAT £70

Assaggi
3

39 Chepstow Pl, London W2 (020) 7792 5501

A big orange room above a pub. The service is scrupulously
courteous and the kitchen puts precision before everything
else, sometimes before flavour. Much of the cooking is plain
to the point of minimalism – grilled calf liver with polenta and
nothing else; tiny lamb cutlets with artichoke hearts; veal with
a little jus and some asparagus.

L AND D MON TO SAT £85

Hsing
4

451 Edgware Rd, London W2 (020) 7402 0983

The menu is gratingly pretentious, the vaguely Thirties' sci-fi
design suggests more style than content. But the cooking is
accomplished in an occidentalised way – this is modern
Chinese cooking as pioneered at the Zen restaurants. Crispy
duck is a superior quacker; Peking raviolis are excellent; there's
a novel dish of mixed fish in ginger and wine. However, signs
of negligence are also in evidence – for instance, very burnt
noodles. The service is efficient, if off-hand.

L AND D TUES TO SUN £50

INAHO

3

4 Hereford Rd, London W2 (020) 7221 8495
Homely Japanese cooking in a tiny wooden cabin off
Westbourne Grove. Unusually, the kitchen employs herbs.
Mostly, though, the stuff is fairly conventional. Portions tend
toward the micro. Service is laid-back, going on supine.

L MON TO FRI, D MON TO SAT £50

KYMA

1

84 Westbourne Grove, London W2 (020) 7792 2207
National colour is laid on with a cheap trowel. The cooking
is off-the-shelf Morrocan – couscous with brochettes, cold
stewed aubergines flavoured with pickled lemons, etc.
Service is gormless.

L AND D EVERY DAY £40

MANDARIN KITCHEN

4

14 Queensway, London W2 (020) 7727 9012
Cantonese fish restaurant done out with Tyrolean finish. A
useful address if you're keen to try such recondite delicacies
as sea slug, a.k.a. sea cucumber, which is blubbery and rather
flavourless. Also: eel fillets with chilli and garlic – this is
excellent – and soft-shelled crabs fried with sesame seeds.
The meat dishes are to be avoided.

L AND D EVERY DAY £46+

MESHWAR

2

128 Edgware Rd, London W2 (020) 7262 8304
It would be easy to overlook this place as a mere takeaway. It
teeters between restaurant and cafe. The menu is the same
menu as at every other place within 400 yards. Cooking is
always precise – aubergines stuffed with walnuts and tomato
are numbingly vinegary, kibbeh greasy, but Armenian sausage
is OK and arayess nice enough.

ALL DAY, EVERY DAY £45

THE OLD DELHI

3

48 Kendal St, London W2 (020) 7723 3335
Buried in a typical 'Indian' menu are a number of Iranian
specialities: lamb with grilled aubergines, lamb with spinach.
Iced rosewater and vermicelli makes a pleasant pudding.

L AND D EVERY DAY £50+

THE PRINCE BONAPARTE

3

80 Chepstow Rd, London W2 (020) 7313 9491

A pub makeover done on the cheap. It still looks like a pub, with the result that Real People wander in to drink keg beer and read the *Sun*. The food is wholesome, fresh, good so far as it goes – which isn't very far. Spaghetti with oil, chilli, basil and clams; baked ricotta with a decently dressed salad; grilled smoked haddock with mash; grilled figs and dates with yoghurt and honey.

L WED TO MON, D EVERY DAY £42+

LOS REMOS

2

38a Southwick St, London W2 (020) 7706 1870

Competent tapas served in an austere basement. The clientele is Spanish middle management, the atmosphere animated.

L AND D MON TO SAT £50

ROYAL CHINA

6

13 Queensway, London W2 (020) 7221 2535

The interior is like a nightclub, but the dim sum are of outstanding quality and at weekends you'll have to queue. The pasta and pastry work are exceptional – pork puffs are little pieces of richly sauced meat. Cheung fun are less slimy than usual. Finish with egg-custard tarts.

L AND D EVERY DAY, DIM SUM NOON TILL 5PM EVERY DAY £30+

TAWANA

3

3 Westbourne Grove, London W2 (020) 7229 3785

Like a small village hall. The decor is short on national colour, the cooking long on flavour. Moo sarong is a pork ball entwined in thin, crisp pasta; spring rolls are crisp and stuffed with noodles and veg. Also recommended: sweetcorn fritters, green curry, coconut and chicken soup, pork with peppers, chillis and deep-fried basil.

L AND D EVERY DAY £50

VERONICA'S

1

3 Hereford Rd, London W2 (020) 7229 5079

Risible 'British' cooking in a Bayswater outfit that seems to have adopted a VE-day theme. The menu is hilariously embarrassing to read. It offers a bizarre combination of dishes from the culinary golden age of the Forties and ones from further back. The kitchen's level of competence is not high.

D EVERY DAY £60+

SW3-SW10

BLAKES

2

33 Roland Gardens, London SW7 (020) 7370 6701

A hotel's basement. It's a Seventies period piece – tastefully
vulgar, cheaply glamorous, black, lacquered. The hard-edged
inkiness tries to recall a bar in Film Noir. Prices are ludicrous
– but that's the point. They guarantee a sort of exclusivity; the
food and wine are secondary to the climactic relief of shooting
a wad of folding stuff. The menu is witlessly international; the
kitchen obsessed by appearances. Presentation is all. It scores
heavily for pretentiousness, too. As an anthology of dated
culinary gimmicks, a meal here is vaguely interesting. But
really it's for the gormless rich.

L AND D EVERY DAY £200

THE BLUE ELEPHANT

5

4 Fulham Broadway, London SW6 (020) 7385 6595

Offshoot of Brussels's top Thai restaurant; the cooking is
mediated by Belgian nous. It is thus far from the peasant-
based gear of most Thai places. Marvellous grilled scallops,
fishcakes and satay owe more to Belgium than to Thailand.
Good lamb with ginger and garlic, and beef with chilli and
baby aubergines. The place is jungle-thick with plants and
the service is by boys in martial uniform. Expensive wines.

L SUN TO FRI, D MON TO THURS £70

THE BOMBAY BRASSERIE

4

Courtfield Rd, London SW7 (020) 7370 4040

Ambitious and expensive subcontinental restaurant – but there
is no guarantee of consistent quality. It can be excellent, but
many people have a thin time here. Chefs trained in different
regional idioms ensure that there is no homogenisation. Spices
are used judiciously. Tandoori dishes can reach real heights.
The vegetable selections are not necessarily appropriate to the
dishes they accompany. Good bread, fine jasmine-tea sorbet.

L AND D EVERY DAY £75+

LA BOUCHEE

1

56 Old Brompton Rd, London SW7 (020) 7589 1929

Crude French cooking in a mainly subterranean bistro. Pig's
trotter looks like something akin to an elephant's used condom.
Pot au feu is poor, pear tart tired, etc.

L AND D EVERY DAY £50

CAFE LAZEEZ

4

93-95 Old Brompton Rd, London SW7 (020) 7581 9993
Lebanese name, Indian cooking – or rather, East/West cooking
where the oriental component comes from the sub-continent.
First in a chain.

L AND D EVERY DAY £60

CAMBIO DE TERCIO

4

163 Old Brompton Rd, London SW5 (020) 7244 8970
Decorated with picadors' banderillas and a toreador's cape.
Ham croquettes are rather bland; grilled squid hesitantly
dressed with parsley and garlic; raw salmon is given a tart
marinade. Hake is overcooked; 'deep-fried milk' is junket
with a cinnamon crust.

L AND D EVERY DAY £70

THE CAPITAL HOTEL

8

22 Basil St, London SW3 (020) 7589 5171
The best privately owned hotel in London. It understands that
the plutocrats who patronise its engagingly odd dining room
eat for amusement rather than nourishment. The cooking is
poised, elegant, delicate, and has affinities with old-fashioned
nouvelle cuisine. The multi-course tasting menus are horribly
named Temptation and Seduction and the dishes invariably
pretentiously described. They taste good, though. There are
almost jammy sorbets and before them bass with black beans
and saffron butter, vegetable 'crème brûlées' which are
mousses, scallops with anchovy mousse, artichokes with herb
mousse. It is assumed that the vinously inclined will not be
seeking bargains.

L AND D EVERY DAY £140+

CHUTNEY MARY

4

525 King's Rd, London SW10 (020) 7351 3113
Billed as the world's 'first Anglo-Indian' restaurant; most
dishes are good, sure-handed and unusual.

L EVERY DAY, D MON TO SAT £70

LE COLOMBIER

5

145 Dovehouse St, London SW3 (020) 7351 1155
A polished former pub behind the hospitals on Fulham Road.
This is far from the usual pub makeover, however – the bar is
not a pub bar, the cooking is not gastropub cooking, the service
is diligent. Rillettes are nicely savoury. A veal chop was a
superb bit of meat. To drink: Domaine Ott's rose, which is
perhaps the most delicious of all roses.

L AND D EVERY DAY £100

DAQUISE   2

20 Thurloe St, London SW7 (020) 7589 6117
Legendary Polish tearoom and restaurant that has been a
home from home for generations of emigrés. Homely cooking
at astonishingly low prices: bortsch, chlodnik, pierogi, stuffed
cabbage, herrings with sour cream, nice cakes. Drink lemon
tea or Tatra beer.

L AND D EVERY DAY £25

GORDON RAMSAY   9

68 Royal Hospital Rd, London SW3 (020) 7352 4441
Unlike the other two hardmen of restauration – Nico Ladenis
and Marco Pierre White – who modelled themselves on
footballers, Ramsay *was* a footballer. The former Rangers
defender can take out unwanted guests with a two-footed
tackle from behind. The inner Ramsay, however, is more a
product of Paris kitchens than Ibrox. Pigeon with braised
cabbage is startlingly delicious. Three sorts of foie gras –
roasted whole lobe, terrine with chicken, and parfait in an
Earl Grey jelly with truffle – are exceptional.

L AND D MON TO FRI £150

ITSU   2

118 Draycott Ave, London SW3 (020) 7584 5522
The restaurant shares Pret a Manger's ownership, though it
harbours very different ambitions. The food travels to your table
via conveyor belts, with hot dishes kept warm by being placed
on frames above nightlights. Standard issue sushi and sashimi
are hunky-dory. The effortful pan-Asian fantasies are not.

L AND D EVERY DAY £45+ (NO BOOKINGS)

LOMO   6

222 Fulham Rd, London SW10 (020) 7349 8848
A Spanish bar that is microwave-free. It is boldly coloured –
elephant and dried blood – and the seating is on high stools at
the bar or counters. Dishes are made with diligence and precision
– and they're an absolute bargain. Salt cod brandade is exceptionally fine; tortilla is a world away from the everyday egg and potato
pudding. Lamb cutlets are of the utmost succulence. Coca turns
out to be crisply-baked bread spread with soft-sweated peppers,
long-cooked sweet onions and anchovies. A treat.

L AND D EVERY DAY (NO BOOKINGS) £25–45

LOU PESCADOU   4

241 Old Brompton Rd, London SW5 (020) 7370 1057
Informal Provençal fish restaurant (whose rare meat dishes are
perfectly sound). Pasta with shellfish, good apple tart.

L AND D EVERY DAY £50

LUNDUMS

8

119 Old Brompton Rd, London SW7 (020) 7373 7774
A welcome surprise. Danish cooking done by a gifted Frenchman,
Frank Dietrich, who doesn't invent but does improve recipes.
Herrings are done with a curried mayo, and with sour cream and
dill. The three sorts of cured salmon – smoked, gravlax and salted –
are top-notch. Pork belly is cooked so that its exterior is crackling.

L EVERY DAY, D MON TO SAT £70

MONKEYS

5

1 Cale St, London SW3 (020) 7352 4711
Shabby, panelled, rather dated Chelsea bistro, some of whose
dishes are good and some of which might be very good, were just
a tiny bit more trouble taken. Châteaubriand is, oddly, served
with nouvelle cuisine-style veg purees; raviolis of lobster and bass
are well flavoured, if inaccurately cooked; the cheeses copiously
portioned and well kept. Chaotic wine list, pleasant service.

£68

MONTPELIANO

3

13 Montpelier St, London SW7 (020) 7589 0032
This Italian joint aims to be fun, and it just about manages it.
The kitchen tries hard, though much of what it turns out is
pretty crude: sweetbreads with prosciutto-like caff bacon,
rather hefty sweets; breadcrumbed brains with lemon butter
are good. Cheap and decent wines.

L AND D EVERY DAY £90

OGNISKO

4

55 Exhibition Rd, London SW7 (020) 7589 4635
The restaurant of the Polish Health Club is open to
non-members and serves excellently prepared traditional
dishes, such as tripe in the Warsaw manner, potato pancakes
with sour cream, wild mushrooms, sauerkraut, flavoured
vodkas. The decor has been modernised a bit and you now
believe yourself in Gdansk in the Fifties.

L AND D EVERY DAY £55

SAN LORENZO

1

22 Beauchamp Place, London SW3 (020) 7584 1074
Arms dealers, horizontales, rock legends, educationally
subnormal royals, ladies who lunch, rag trade morons, ladies
who shop, actors, supermodels, beautiful persons. If you have
not appeared in *Hello!*, you might as well forget it, since the
charmless staff will do their utmost to ignore you. The cooking
is not the point of the place, which is just as well.

L AND D MON TO SAT £100

STAR OF INDIA

7

154 Old Brompton Rd, London SW5 (020) 7373 2901

High camp decor – all Italianate frescos and distressed trompe l'oeil. At night it's a hangout for celebrity weather girls and the rest of the braindead. So go at lunchtime for some of the most delicious sub-continental cooking in town. The cooking is clear-flavoured, robust, novel, gimmick-free. Methi mass is a tremendously savoury lamb stew with the consistency of a Malaysian rendang; gosht parda biryani is a rice and lamb pie with sweet pastry. Salmon is marinated, smoked, cooked in a tandoor till its skin is black. Also worth trying: a meaty combination of aubergine and paneer cheese, scallops with coriander seeds and dill, spiced pineapple.

L AND D EVERY DAY £80+

TURNER'S

6

87-89 Walton St, London SW3 (020) 7849 3810

Flashy customers, accomplished French cooking, stingy portions and a telly chef-patron who spends most of his time in his immaculate whites greeting his customers. Rabbit terrine, duck pâté, well-sauced bream and mullet, successfully elaborate sweets, fine cheeses. Unexciting wines.

L AND D MON TO SAT £95

VAMA

3

438 King's Rd, London SW10 (020) 7351 4118

The first London enterprise by a Delhi family whose restaurants in that city are Italian. The dining room is airy and uncluttered: it would work equally well as a trattoria. There's a further and odder Italian connection: tomato and herbs on a paratha was uncannily like a pizza – quite a decent pizza, mind. An excess of tomato didn't spoil a chicken curry, but granted no favours to dhal. Marinated fish in (tomato paste?) batter was top-notch: subtle, moist, savoury. Mango khulfi is almost excessively rich. Masala tea is a better bet.

L AND D EVERY DAY £75+

ZIANI

5

45 Radnor Walk, London SW3 (020) 7352 2698

Good place for bollito misto and char-grilled steaks. It is hideously cramped so you can smell the next table's breath. Commonplace wines at decent prices.

L AND D EVERY DAY £70

W8–W11

'192'   4
192 Kensington Park Rd, London W11 (020) 7229 0482
Persistently fashionable hangout with ever-younger clientele.
Numerous starry chefs have cut their teeth here. The cooking
shows promise but not much more. Good ideas are carelessly
executed. Lamb's brain with capers is sound enough.

L AND D EVERY DAY £65+

AIX EN PROVENCE   5
**The Halcyon Hotel, 129 Holland Park Ave, London
W11** (020) 7221 5411
A light basement decorated in a pleasant off-the-peg manner. It
tries to pretend that it is something other than a hotel restaurant.
Instead, you get a fairly modish repertoire done with real effort,
though with inconsistent results. The wines are expensive.

L AND D EVERY DAY £80

ALASTAIR LITTLE   9
136a Lancaster Rd, London W11 (020) 7243 2220
The second restaurant of the most copied chef of the past
decade. The room is understated; cooking is balanced, unflashy,
eager to please. The customer can count on things along the
lines of tongue with salsa verde; boiled mutton with caper sauce
(excellent); a minestrone which includes greens, haricot beans
and skate; butch salads of chicken livers and duck confit;
Spanish charcuterie: fritto misto of vegetables; first-rate blood
orange sorbet. Wines and cheeses are well chosen. The place is
relaxed and friendly. Prices are most reasonable.

L EVERY DAY, D MON TO SAT £80

BRASSERIE DU MARCHE AUX PUCES   4
349 Portobello Rd, London W10 (020) 8968 5828
Easy-going and unpretentious outfit in the heart of a burglary
belt. The furniture here is decidedly not worth stealing. The
food is straightforward and, for the most part, rather better
than might be expected in so casual an outfit. Flavour-free
frogs' legs are steamed and given a posthumous bath in garlic
butter. Gravlax with lemon-flavoured crème fraîche is
commendable, and so, too, is chicken with lemon, cinnamon
and honey. Andouillettes are served with fried potatoes and
mushrooms. Decent cheap wines.

L EVERY DAY, D MON TO SAT £60

CALZONE
2

2a Kensington Park Rd, London W11 (020) 7243 2003
Straightforward and admirably restrained pizzas in a goldfish
bowl at Notting Hill Gate. The bases are thin, chapati-like.
Toppings are intensely flavoured, composed of manifestly
fresh ingredients. The place is cramped, neat, eau de nil.

L AND D EVERY DAY £20+

CASA SANTANA
2

44 Golborne Rd, London W10 (020) 8968 8764
Portuguese cafe-cum-restaurant. Dead basic grub, totally
unrefined. Feijoada is a bean stew along the lines of God's first
try at cassoulet. The grilled squid is good and so are the
amazingly cheap wines.

L AND D EVERY DAY £32

CHEZ MOI
6

1 Addison Ave, London W11 (020) 7603 8267
Soigné, theatrical decor; plump, pleased clients; individualistic
cooking. The kitchen's manner is probably little altered since
the place opened in the mid-Sixties, and is none the worse
for that: excellent civit of hare; delicious croquettes called
kromanski; amazing lemon tart. Pretty good service, too.

L TUES TO FRI, D MON TO SAT £70

CLARKE'S
5

124 Kensington Church St, London W8 (020) 7221 9225
No choice dinners, limited choice lunches. The cooking is
superior dinner party stuff; fairly simple, well balanced, good
ingredients, not much showing off. Ricotta and artichoke pie,
well-herbed rack of lamb, first-rate British cheeses, nice
breads. If you can accept the rather tyrannical premise, it is
a worthwhile establishment. Sound wine list, strong in New
World bargains.

L AND D MON TO FRI £100

GALICIA
4

323 Portobello Rd, London W10 (020) 8969 3539
Authentically unambitious cooking from northwest Spain.
Curiously authentic atmosphere, too: the fact that most of the
punters are Spanish helps. Fish is cooked with some degree
of basic skill; meat isn't. The wines are cheap and portions are
large. A good-looking joint in a serious, unfashionable way.

L AND D TUES TO SUN £50

HIROKO

4

Kensington Hilton, 179 Holland Park Ave, London W11
(020) 7603 5003

Good-quality Japanese cooking served in boothed, light wood
dining room approached through the airport-like hotel. Tartare
steak with sesame, fine sashimi, aubergine with soya paste.

L AND D TUES TO SUN £60

KENSINGTON PLACE

10

201 Kensington Church St, London W8 (020) 7727 3184
The premises have expanded seamlessly to accommodate
about 140 covers. It is still incredibly noisy, incredibly
fashionable and incredibly party-like – it is the most enjoyable
restaurant in London by some way. The mix of customers is
unmatched; the service is attentive and pretty swift; the
cocktails first rate. The fact that it is such a social success
means that the kitchen probably gets taken for granted when,
in more reverential surroundings, the food it produces would
be universally acknowledged as top-notch. The wine list is
quirky, full of decently priced oddities.

L AND D EVERY DAY £75, SET LUNCH £40

MALABAR

2

27 Uxbridge St, London W8 (020) 7727 8800
Almost austere decor and a brief menu of rarely seen items.
The cooking is hit and miss – the most succesful dishes are
the most commonplace.

L AND D EVERY DAY £50+

ORSINO

4

119 Portland Rd, London W11 (020) 7221 3299
Handsome, elbow-grabbing design. A quintessentially urban
restaurant plonked down in a suburban street in Holland Park.
It is the baby sibling of Orso in Covent Garden and its menu
is pretty similar. The emphasis is on grilled meats, upmarket
pizzas and antipasti that tend to be assemblies rather than
cooked dishes. When cooking is essayed, the results are mixed:
hare with a chocolate sauce and polenta is good; risotto with
fungi is OK.

L AND D EVERY DAY £80

PHARMACY

4

150 Notting Hill Gate, London W11 (020) 7221 2442
Damien Hirst has delivered a sleekly themed bar and dining
room which are nicely witty, doucely playful and oddly smooth.
The only freakish aspect of the outfit is the sheer number of
diners who look as though they are on Hollywood's F-list and
who presumably come here because it reminds their dull

brains of being at the cosmetic surgeon's. Spit-roast sea bass
was pretty good – crisply skinned, fresh and properly
succulent; grilled rib-eye with braised chard was notable for
the quality of the meat. Lamb is roasted slowly, but perhaps
not slowly enough – the meat was fibrous rather than fondant.

L AND D EVERY DAY £100

STICKY FINGERS

2

1a Phillimore Gardens, London W8 (020) 7938 5338

Bill Wyman's restaurant is a shrine to himself and to the rest
of the Rolling Stones – photos, news clippings, gold discs,
pubic souvenirs, guitars; there's nothing that can't be put in a
frame. It's a loud and pretty frantic place: part burger joint,
part spare ribs diner, part cajun shack. By the standards of
such gastronomic subcultures it's not too bad at all.

L AND D EVERY DAY £50

THE VALE

2

99 Chippenham Rd, London W9 (020) 7266 0990

The premises comprise two conservatories added to a former
corner shop. The internal space is awkward, unresolved, bitty;
the kitchen overkeen to impress and has yet to learn
reticence. Calf's kidney is properly timed and served with
potato puree – that would be enough, but value is added in
the form of beetroot sauce, horseradish cream, flavourless
green beans. Skate and chorizo is a combination that doesn't
come off. Desserts are more confidently achieved.

L TUE TO FRI AND SUN, D MON TO SAT £75+

WODKA

5

12 St Albans Grove, London W8 (020) 7937 6513

Smart and fashionable joint serving rather elevated Polish and
Russian dishes. The decorative style is industrial chic. Wines
are mostly New World, the flavoured vodkas trad; the
cooking is well-gauged: pierogi of sauerkraut and mushrooms,
coulibiac of salmon, fishcakes, black pudding. Groovy staff,
cool customers.

L MON TO FRI, D EVERY DAY £70

Elsewhere

Adam's Cafe

2

77 Askew Rd, London W12 (020) 8743 0572
By day a greasy caff, by night a Tunisian couscous restaurant.
It is very cheap, very amiable and the cooking (brik à l'oeuf,
couscous itself) is pleasant enough.

D MON TO SAT £20

Alounak Kebab

4

10 Russell Gardens, London W14 (020) 7371 2350
First courses are rudimentary. The real point of the place is its
grilled meat, which is first rate: thin strips of fillet steak and
minced lamb kebabs are generously served and accompanied
by rice. You can bring your own alcohol.

ALL DAY, EVERY DAY £25

the Anglesea Arms

9

35 Wingate Rd, London W6 (020) 8749 1291
The best pub restaurant in London. Foie gras terrine with
truffle oil; beef stovey which is a sort of lobscouse with fried
egg on top of a beef and potato hash – both are outstandingly
good. The interior comprises leather sofas and log fires.
Service tends to get chaotic under pressure.

L AND D EVERY DAY £60

Azou

6

375 King St, London W6 (020) 8563 7266
A tiny shop conversion between Hammersmith and Chiswick.
The first thing to be said in its favour is that not much money
has been spent on fitting it out. The second is that national
colour has been only sparingly sprayed on. There is Franco-
Moorish pop music – but it's not that irritating. The Algerian
chef offers three tagines from Tunisia, four from Morocco,
four from his own country. They are splendid. With them
come the lightest couscous and excellent cakey bread.

L MON TO FRI, D EVERY DAY £55, SET MEALS £40

Bedlington Cafe

2

24 Fauconberg Rd, London W4 (020) 8994 1965
By day a greasy caff, by night a Thai diner. The Thai cooking
has some affinities with grease cooking – notably in the deep-
fried battered dishes. The 'red' and 'green' curries are all right,
although might be improved if the frozen peas were omitted.

L AND D EVERY DAY £22+

THE BRACKENBURY 6

129-131 Brackenbury Rd, London W6 (020) 8748 0107
A rather pretty former wine bar in a Pooterish backwater
between Hammersmith and Shepherd's Bush. The cooking is
good. The real delights are such things as soufflé-like pancakes
made with potato and egg and served with salmon roe, or roast
hake with pesto-flavoured mash. Duck confit is well flavoured,
dover sole done with a herb crust.

L SUN AND TUES TO FRI, D MON TO SAT £60

BUSH BAR AND GRILL 6

45a Goldhawk Rd, London W12 (020) 8746 2111
A former light industrial building has been transformed with
butch know-how. It is imagination that has been thrown at it
rather than money: red-painted breeze blocks, powder-blue
painted plank ceiling, cheapish chairs. The menu is seductive.
Everything it offers is straightforward, and everything that
arrives on the table is correct: tomato soup with crème fraîche,
celeriac remoulade with rocket salad, fishcakes, a herb
omelette. The service was sweet.

L AND D EVERY DAY £55, SET MEALS £40

CAFE ROUGE 0

85 Strand-on-the-Green, London W4 (020) 8995 6575
I can't think of any circumstance which would cause me to
again patronise one of these Harvesters for the indiscriminate
middle classes. It took me, having eaten precisely one chip,
four hours and a dozen bodybuilder-strength mints to get rid
of the horrible taste. Branches grow like weeds.

L AND D EVERY DAY £40+

CHINON 7

23 Richmond Way, London W14 (020) 7602 5968
The cooking is unusually ornate. Every dish has numerous
components. The appeal is akin to that of a child's puzzle –
you keep finding extra bits and pieces. More often than not
this ancient nouvelle cuisine comes off very well; the fact that
it's now so old-fashioned as to be new-fashioned is neither
here nor there. The chef has pretty consistent taste and keeps
a rein on his imagination, although a fondness for raw leek
might suggest otherwise. Squid, salmon and venison are all
confidently handled. The puddings are ostentatious.

D MON TO SAT £75

THE CHISWICK   5

131 Chiswick High Rd, London W4 (020) 8994 6887
Plain, hard-edged, not exactly comforting, and for a large
space, it seems cramped. Also, the tables are very small. Cod
is skilfully and simply roasted and served with a potato puree
so full of olive oil it has the consistency of mayo. Veal offal is
served with a savoury, soufflé'd pancake. There is good gravlax
and a winning 'ragoût' of snails, piquant chorizo and tomato.

L SUN TO FRI, D MON TO SAT £55+

CIBO   6

3 Russell Gardens, London W14 (020) 7371 6271
Often exciting Italian cooking in a decorative hotchpotch across
the railtracks from Olympia. Some dishes are specifically north
Italian, others might be found in starry restaurants anywhere
between Bologna and Brussels. Among the many excellent
dishes from a frequently changing menu: raw marinated salmon,
tuna and scallops; grilled Asiago cheese with sweated sweet
peppers; ceps fried with garlic; beef with stewed ceps; mullet
with extra virgin oil and garlic. The vegetables are inventive.

L SUN TO FRI, D MON TO SAT £75

DELIVERANCE   3

www.deliverance.co.uk (0800) 019 2222
An enterprise that posts its menus on the Web, though you
order by phone or fax. It has six or so kitchens, each devoted to
a different kind of cooking – Italian, 'European', Thai, etc. The
menus are short with photographs of the chefs. The Indian chef's
name suggested he might be Goanese, so I ordered Goan chick-
en curry. This was pleasant enough. A seekh kebab of minced
lamb was really rather good. The Chinese dishes were flavoured
so as not to offend. The messenger who brought what the company describes as 'culinary salvation' was French and polite.

L SAT AND SUN, D EVERY DAY. £40.

THE GLASSHOUSE   8

14 Station Parade, Kew (020) 8940 6777
The front and side are entirely glazed, in signal contrast to the
cheerily ordinary red brick above. Chef Anthony Boyd is one
to watch. A brochette of lamb offal and merguez with couscous
and a meaty sauce is real high-definition cooking. The timing
was spot on. Coq au vin was ace – the meat was marinated,
the sauce rich, unctuous, based on something worth drinking.
Prices are amiable.

L AND D EVERY DAY £70+

GOLDEN PALACE

8

146 Station Rd, Harrow, HA1 (020) 8863 2333

In a world where there's not much worth queuing for, this place surely is. What it's doing in the wrong end of Harrow is anybody's guess. The cooking tastes like good cooking – not like Chinese cooking. It is true to its ingredients, light, delicate, individualistic. Standard items set new standards – cheung fun, 'charcoal'-roast duck; scallops with braised garlic.

L AND D EVERY DAY, DIM SUM WEEKENDS TILL 5PM £46

THE HAVELOCK TAVERN

4

57 Masbro Rd, London W14 (020) 7603 5374

Pub conversion in an area of bijou ouvrier dwellings between Shepherd's Bush Green and Olympia. A great show of casualness is made, but the kitchen is profesional and knocks out rustic food with some brio. A salad of duck hearts with duck gizzards, poached egg, beans and croutons is top-notch gear. And a rather similar collation with pot-roast tuna is also pleasing. Fishcakes are well made with smoked haddock.

L AND D EVERY DAY £50+

KOZACHOK

1

10 Red Lion St, Richmond (020) 8948 2366

Cafe decorated with panels depicting bibulous Russian scenes. The stuffed pasta, pelmeni or varenyki are all right. Lots of flavoured vodkas, and some rare Russian wines.

D TUES TO SAT £50

LOWICZANKA

5

238-246 King St, London W6 (020) 8741 3225

The restaurant of the Polish Social and Cultural Centre. The clientele is largely composed of Polish families, who are served by matronly ladies in 'authentic' costume. The food is copious tripe, stuffed cabbage, cured sausage, potato pancakes, sweet pancakes. There are numerous flavoured vodkas to choose from.

L AND D EVERY DAY £30+

MAQUIS

4

111 Hammersmith Grove, London W6 (020) 8846 3851

The repertoire chosen by Maquis is a pick-and-mix selection which, incidentally, makes no reference to the southern maquis from which restaurants took their name. This is not to say that it is ill executed, indeed some dishes are done with passable competence. But the idiom, like it or not, is Franglais.

L EVERY DAY, D MON TO SAT £70

McCLEMENTS

7

2 Whitton Rd, Twickenham, TW1 (020) 8744 9610

The trip to the suburbs is rewarded with butch cooking done with taste and flair. Appetiser: mashed-up gizzards with good home-baked bread. There is first-rate black pudding (again, home-made) served in a pastry crust with a mustard sauce. Two very good pork dishes: head - i.e., muzzle, cheek, cerebral medulla – with a meaty sauce and garlicky potato puree; or grilled loin in broth with the addition of a slice of cod – it works very well, odd to relate. Various other potatoes are exemplary. Sauces are flavourful. The cheeses are superior to the puddings. Wines are cheap.

L MON TO FRI, D MON TO SAT £70

MONSIEUR MAX

8

133 High St, Hampton Hill, TW12 (020) 8979 5546

Max Renzland's solo debut aims to turn back the clock to France of the mid-Fifties: veal blanquette, gratin dauphinois, properly hung beef, rillettes, celeriac remoulade, etc. The prices are reasonable, service is friendly. Recommended – if you can find it.

L SUN TO FRI, D TUES TO SAT £80

MUSHA

4

133 Uxbridge Rd, London W13 (020) 8566 3788

Obliterate your senses with 'hot potato spirit' or with plum spirit. A hotpot of greens and mixed fish is dressed with chilli flakes; cod roe in a chilli marinade is OK; smelt fish is a sardine relation; red bean ice cream and red bean jelly are for the very curious.

L WED TO SUN, D WED TO MON £50

NIGHTINGALES

2

Petersham Hotel, Nightingale Lane, Richmond
(020) 8940 7471

High Victorian hotel by the same hand that devised the Langham. It is a brash blot. The interior is all 1980s hoteliers' 'good taste'. The clientele is mostly international businessmen and local trouser-rollers. Service is pretty appalling. Some of the cooking is spirited – a fishcake with a parsley sauce, for instance. But more usually it is typical hotel stuff, anxious not to offend with flavour. The views west along the Thames are splendid.

L EVERY DAY, D MON TO SAT £75+

THE POPESEYE   6
108 Blythe Rd, London W14 (020) 7610 4578
Popeseye is a Scottish name for beef rump. This excellently
idiosyncratic joint offers three cuts of beef in different sizes,
chips, green salad, farmhouse cheeses, puddings such as fruit
fools. And that's it. Everything is spot-on and the chargrilled
meat is of outstanding quality. The wines are cannily selected
and include a dozen or so clarets at friendly prices.

D MON TO SAT (CASH OR CHEQUE ONLY) £55+

PREGO   1
106 Kew Rd, Richmond (020) 8948 8508
All of the mannerisms of conventional middle-brow
restauration – bowls of unadulterated olive oil and iffy bread
to dip in it, potent espresso coffee – but little of the content.
Much of the food is 'chargrilled'. Fishcakes are rather nasty;
duck breast comes with 'garlic smashed potato', which isn't
Smash, thankfully.

L AND D EVERY DAY £63+

THE RED PEPPER   3
8 Formosa St, London W9 (020) 7266 2708
Cramped black hole of Catania posing as a predominantly
pizza restaurant in a Maida Vale shopping street. It is startlingly
uncomfortable and its popularity is ascribable exclusively to the
food. The pizzas are first rate, and so are such things as squid
stuffed with garlicky breadcrumbs.

L SAT AND SUN, D EVERY DAY £65

THE RIVER CAFE   9
Thames Wharf, Rainville Rd, London W6 (020) 7381 8824
The most imitated Italian restaurant in London, which has a
bar/servery designed by Richard Rogers. The cooking is
tremendous. The kitchen doesn't get between the food and the
customer; it quite properly trusts its suppliers. Oils, wines,
vinegars, meats, fish, vegetables are of the highest quality and
you pay for the ability to leave well alone. Some of the best
dishes include: calf's kidney done in a Roman manner with mint
and chilli and a fricassee of ceps and field mushrooms; sea bass
grilled with capers, rocket and peppers; polenta cake flavoured
with lemon. Flavours are constantly true, powerful, fresh.

L EVERY DAY, D MON TO SAT £120

SNOWS ON THE GREEN

5

166 Shepherd's Bush Rd, London W6 (020) 7603 2142
Pleasant place, nice prices, enticing menu. The cooking is not,
however, consistent. Seasoning is liable to be non-existent. When
things come together, the results are splendid: salt-cod brandade,
chartreuse of partridge, lamb with an aubergine and mozzarella
gratin.

L MON TO FRI, D MON TO SAT £65

YAS

3

7 Hammersmith Rd, London W14 (020) 7603 3980
Appealing Persian pickles; a dish of rice which turns into a sort
of fried rice pudding; lamb stew with aubergines; ice cream with
a consistency like mayonnaise. All these are worth trying.

L AND D EVERY DAY £50

ZAIKA

5

1 Kensington High St, London W8 (020) 7351 7823
There are some treats here. Tandoori smoked salmon is a
delicious dish fighting its way out from beneath oversweet
sauces; minced duck rolls are so overspiced that they might
have been made from any meat. A nan bread with a paneer
stuffing was great. Service is slow. The lassi is very nice
indeed.

L SUN TO FRI, D EVERY DAY £80

ENGLAND

South East

Berkshire

THE FAT DUCK
5

High St, Bray (01628) 580333
Unpainted beams, gourds, teasels, mottled walls,
uncomfortable wrought-steel chairs. The taste is metropolitan,
rather than home counties. Cooking is massively ambitious
and when things go right it's impressive. But at these prices
consistency is required, and it is not forthcoming – there are
persistent flaws of conception and execution. Desserts are
good. A dish of brined duck with the most exquisite potato
puree is marred by the mistiming of the meat. Guinea fowl is
done in a terrible curry sauce. If a kitchen is going to rely as
heavily as this one does on deep-frying, then it needs to learn
to do it greaselessly.

L TUES TO SUN, D TUES TO SAT £100+

THE LEATHERNE BOTTEL

6

The Bridleway, Goring-on-Thames (01491) 872667

Easy-going and pleasant riverside restaurant, handsomely
converted from a pub. In summer one can eat outside with
the ducks and pleasure cruisers. The cooking is strong on
chargrilling, steaming, abundant herbs and colourful
assemblies of vegetables. It is not so strong on sauces, nor on
dressings. By Thames Valley standards, it is reasonably priced.

L EVERY DAY, D MON TO SAT £70

THE SWAN HOTEL

2

Streatley on Thames, Reading (01491) 878800

The view is of a stereotypical Thamescape: weir, weeping
willow, Oxford barge, motor cruiser. Service is officious and
the cooking's laudable gutsiness is marred by a tendency to
over-emphatic saucing and a certain brutality of flavour. But
such things as fish soup are all right.

L AND D EVERY DAY £90

THE TERRACE DINING ROOM

4

Cliveden Hotel, Taplow (01628) 668561

Stately is for once the apt word. And of course Cliveden also
has its own notoriety, its gardens, its drive, its formidable view.
It is both a National Trust property and a hotel: trippers gape
at diners and no doubt burst into bedrooms at crucial
moments. This is the less formal, less luxurious of its two
restaurants – which suggests that the other is exclusively for
the inhabitants of Planet Dosh. This one mixes exemplary
steak and chips with such things as sea bass with truffle oil,
foie gras in various guises, humble tomato soup with pistou.
The staff is vast, attentive, well-drilled, dressed with almost
heraldic formality. Enjoyable, expensive.

L AND D EVERY DAY £125+

THE VINEYARD

8

Stockcross, Newbury (01635) 528770

Even if the wine list was not among the best in the country,
this restaurant would be worth patronising for its cooking.
Chef Billy Reid turns out an array of accomplished dishes:
beef carpaccio with parmesan; anchovy fritters; langoustine
brochette; light sole in batter; savoury braised lamb. Nothing is
embellished and everything gets to the table hot. Les Pavots
from owner Peter Michael's Californian winery is a liquid of
such poise that 99.9 per cent of the rest of the stuff in bottles
is at a stroke rendered vinously subnormal. Point Rouge
Chardonnay is also an exceptional drop.

L AND D EVERY DAY £110

THE WATERSIDE INN

10

Ferry Rd, Bray, Maidenhead (01628) 620691
Michel Roux's deluxe outfit is the ne plus ultra of the
Home Counties restaurant, often aped, but never matched.
Customers tend to be overdressed, service is copious and
formal and the cooking often seems to belong to a different
era. The more 'worked', the more baroque a dish, the
better it is likely to be. Lobster ravioli are terrific. So is
calf kidney, which is roasted whole and served with
deep-fried sweetbreads and braised lettuce on a sauce
diable. The puddings include a great dish of pasta stuffed
with lemon curd. The wine list is long, posh and very
expensive. A great treat.

L AND D WED TO SUN £190+

BUCKINGHAMSHIRE

STOKE PARK BRASSERIE

3

Stoke Park Club, Park Rd, Stoke Poges (01753) 717171
The dining room is hung with prewar travel posters and is
overseen by a French Gary Neville clone (he is rather better at
his job, though). The cooking, by hotel standards, is good. By
golf club standards, it is stellar. A Caesar salad was OK, though
made with too soft a species of lettuce. Cod was done with a
well-made parsley sauce, broad beans and indifferent mash.
Strawberry jelly was delicious. There's a reasonable wine list
and potent coffee.

L MON TO FRI, D EVERY DAY £85, SET LUNCH £55

GUERNSEY

LE NAUTIQUE

3

Quay Steps, St Peter Port (0481) 721714
Converted warehouse with a Seventies interior. An
outpost of Italian Soho, even though the menu is written in
French. Some of the food is indifferent: risotto is akin to a
third-division pilaff; sea bass is overdone. Some of it is
acceptable: skate with black butter; deep-fried monkfish with
tartare sauce; crab and prawn gratin. Puddings are along the
lines of profiteroles. There are some enterprisingly chosen
New World wines.

L MON TO FRI, D MON TO SAT £60+

HAMPSHIRE

36 ON THE QUAY
7

47 South St, Emsworth (01243) 375592

Stiff, formal, pretentious – yet also very likeable. The dining
room of this yachting-village cottage is handsomely done out
and the very grand cooking is executed with apparent ease.
There are gratefully received courses of amuse-bouches and
friandises, and between them beautifully gauged items such
as poached salmon with olive oil dressing and potato pancakes
with (excellent) smoked salmon. The best restaurant between
Brighton and Southampton.

L TUES TO FRI, D MON TO SAT £90

ALLERTON'S, GRAND HARBOUR HOTEL
0

West Quay Rd, Southampton (02380) 633033

This hotel is a major eyesore. It is one of the ugliest buildings
in Britain. Its restaurant's strong point is the view of medieval
walls. Service is chaotic and slow. The cooking is inept – fish
is grossly overcooked, crab wontons are nasty, sauteed potatoes
are greasy.

L AND D TUES TO SAT £100

THE AUGUSTUS JOHN
5

Station Rd, Fordingbridge (01425) 652098

This pub was formerly The Railway Hotel and it was John's
local. It has been transformed into a pub-restaurant of
handsome austerity: this is the way to do it. And this is the
way to cook in such places – to offer a short menu of
un-mucked-about, un-gimmicked dishes which are well
executed and copiously served at knock-down prices.

L AND D EVERY DAY £30

CHEWTON GLEN
9

Christchurch Rd, New Milton (01425) 275341

This is *the* luxury hotel. Despite a rather unpromising setting
in the sprawl of outer Bournemouth, it sets the standard for
all British 'country-house' hotels. Service is astonishing. The
place works like a well-oiled machine, yet there is nothing
impersonal about it. The cooking is luxury hotel stuff but done
with a flair and talent that are rare: scallops with shredded
mangetouts and butter sauce; raviolis of fennel; millefeuille
of salmon and spinach; sweetbreads with vinegar sauce; terrific
puddings.

L AND D EVERY DAY £125, LUNCH IS LESS

THE GAME LARDER

2

New St, Stockbridge (01264) 810414

An 18th-century brewhouse done up with ancient timbers to look like a medieval hall. The cooking teeters on the right side of adequate, the service is friendly; a good place to go in a large party.

L WED TO SUN, D TUES TO SAT £80

HOTEL DU VIN AND BISTRO

7

Southgate St, Winchester (01962) 841414

This hotel is sticking to the task of beating the chains at their own prices. A fish soup is as good as fish soup gets. An odd mix of pork, chorizo and sauerkraut is a great deal better than it sounds. Cod done in tempura batter with aioli and chips could not be improved. The choice of bargain price wines is compendious.

L AND D EVERY DAY £65

LAINSTON HOUSE

2

Sparsholt, Winchester (01962) 863588

Rather beautiful early 18th-century house in impressive parkland. The cooking is Anglo-French and competent. The same might be said of the interior of the building and the service.

L AND D EVERY DAY £80+

MASTER BUILDER'S HOUSE HOTEL

2

Buckler's Hard, Beaulieu (01590) 616253

The hotel has a built-in pub with a yachtie clientele in blinding all-weather gear and a fully acredited sea dog propping up the bar. The kitchen is 'overseen' by Kevin Mangeolles, the impressive chef at The George at Yarmouth. He has failed to pass on his knack. Bass was good, but the 'risotto' with it was bizarre – dry, cakey, flavoured with almonds. Ribeye steak was flavourless and attended by an aggressive lemon butter. Chips were raw in the middle; cheeses came straight from the fridge.

L AND D EVERY DAY £70

MONTAGU ARMS

6

Palace Lane, Beaulieu (01590) 612324

Not quite what you expect in a Fully Accredited Beauty Spot. This is a good hotel with a highly promising restaurant. The cooking is polished, and, in the case of fish dishes, really excellent: salmon with delicate pasta, smoked salmon and crab tart. Vegetables are often inspired and the sweets are nice. However, both duck and guinea fowl were pretty flavourless; maybe a new supplier is called for. A fine selection of wines including numerous half bottles. Good natured and well-informed service.

L AND D EVERY DAY £80

THE OLD MANOR HOUSE   6
21 Palmerston St, Romsey (01794) 517353
Beamed dining rooms, uneasily formal yet friendly service,
terrific wine list, variable cooking. The simpler, mainly Italian,
dishes are a match for anywhere: pasta, risotto with porcini,
cotechino with lentils, etc. The more complicated and more
expensive ones are all right, but nothing more. Stick to the
cheaper menus at lunchtime when two can eat well for £45.

L TUES TO SUN, D TUES TO SAT £50, D IS £70+

THE PEAT SPADE INN   2
Longstock, near Stockbridge (01264) 810612
Dinner-party food in the Test Valley. Rillettes, langoustine
terrine, chargrilled meat. The ingredients are good and, while the
kitchen is not especially skilled, it doesn't muck things up. There's
good beer from the Andover Brewery and a rather odd wine list.

L TUES TO SUN, D TUES TO SAT £50

SIMPLY POUSSIN   8
The Courtyard, Off Brookley Rd, Brockenhurst
(01590) 623063
Small, resourceful and unusual. This is one of the few
genuinely regional restaurants in Britain. The surrounding
New Forest provides game, pig, mushrooms, and the sea is
only a few miles away. Alex Aitken is a skilled and inventive
chef who keeps things admirably simple. Deer kidney, deer
heart, deer fillet are sauced with a port reduction; soups are
good, so are soufflés, so is bread. There is a patently wholehearted approach to even the smallest details. Decent wines.

L AND D TUES TO SAT £60

THE THREE LIONS   8

Stuckton, Fordingbridge (01425) 652489

Not really a pub, despite the name and despite the awkward convention of displaying the menu on a blackboard in the cramped bar. Michael Womersley cooks like a dream and, unlike many provincial restaurateurs, enjoys a demanding audience – the Avon valley and the New Forest is full of second-home owners who expect metropolitan standards. Womersley worked for Raymond Blanc and was head chef at Lucknam Park. He does not, however, make the mistake of essaying grand hotel cooking in this berth. The food is admirably straightforward, technically consummate, deliciously flavoured. This is a chef with an infallible palate. Salmon may be mi-cuit, roast on one side only with a tomato and olive 'jam', or it may be done raw with tarragon and a mousse-like cream. Duck parfait is served with a brioche which has lemon in the mix; lamb escalope (a first?) is served with a peppery sauce. An epic lamb knuckle outdoes every kleftiko. Crème brûlée is unusually and successfully flavoured with tarragon.

L TUES TO SUN, D TUES TO SAT £70

ISLE OF WIGHT

THE GEORGE HOTEL   6

Quay St, Yarmouth (01983) 760331

The best cooking on the island. Chef Kevin Mangeolles goes for big, butch flavours, though is not immune to delicate touches – his home-smoked salmon with potato and truffle salad is very good. More typical is fechoulette of lamb, which includes stuffed neck, kidney, liver, thymus. Duck suffers from being cooked at too low a temperature, though duck, ham and rillettes were fine.

L AND D MON TO SAT £80

KENT

HONOURS MILL   4

87 High St, Edenbridge (01732) 866757

A beautifully converted clapboard mill in commuterland. The cooking is polished, but rather timid in its flavouring, as if it does not want to offend. Fish tends to be better than meat – red mullet with a red wine sauce, smoked fishes in jelly, etc. Impressive wines, courteous service.

L TUES TO FRI AND SUN, D TUES TO SAT £75+

HOTEL DU VIN AND BISTRO 7
Crescent Rd, Tunbridge Wells (01892) 526455

No frills are admitted. The repertoire is butch, and unfashionably meaty. But it is also informed by real finesse, by a most evident generosity. The sweetest lamb rack is served with a potato puree flavoured with rosemary; venison is braised, sticky, gamey, potent. Foie gras, roasted with apples and beetroot, is first-rate. The wines are all that might be expected from a team which includes the former sommeliers of Chewton Glen and Le Manoir aux Quat' Saisons. Prices are low.

L AND D EVERY DAY £65

KENNEL HOLT HOTEL 6
Goudhurst Rd, Cranbrook (01580) 712032

A well-hidden Wealden house surrounded by topiarised yews. The kitchen is slick and the owners, staff and wonder dog are both relaxed and eagerly accommodating. A raviolo of well-made pasta is stuffed with ricotta and spinach, and served with a tomato sauce pepped up with chilli vinegar; a savoury terrine comes with marinated chanterelles.

D TUES TO SAT (LUNCH BY PRIOR ARRANGEMENT
– PARTIES OF 6+ ONLY) £65+

ROYAL NATIVE OYSTER STORES 6
Horse Bridge, Whitstable (01227) 276856

A utilitarian Victorian building on a shingle beach with views across the Thames estuary and to Sheppey. The menu is unmitigatingly piscine. Oysters, of course, outstanding salmon smoked on the premises, first-rate deep-frying, scallops, baby plaice, whiting, octopus. Everything is done with total conviction and no fuss.

L TUES TO SUN, D TUES TO SAT (SUN FROM JUNE–AUGUST) £90+

SANDGATE HOTEL 8
The Esplanade, Sandgate, Folkestone (01303) 220444

An almost entirely French hotel which gazes out to the channel (and Dungeness). Chef Samuel Gicqueau's cooking is ambitiously complex, but bereft of redundant flourishes. Guinea fowl is done with morel mousse, morel sauce and ravioli stuffed with morels – yet it is not at all on one note. Lobster ravioli are intensely rather than richly sauced; scallops and turbot are good. The restaurant values the laurels of Michelin, so is fussy, formal and precious.

L TUES TO SUN, D TUES TO SAT £90+

SIGNOR FRANCO
5a High St, Tunbridge Wells (01892) 549199

6

A sort of Edwardian conservatory above a parade of shops. The owner is immensely hospitable. The menu is not particularly adventurous but the quality of the cooking is consistently high. Poached squid with salsa verde; salted cured pork sausage with a mighty stew of borlotti beans; risotto with shaved black truffle – these are all first rate. Good range of Sicilian amari.

L AND D MON TO SAT £70

THE WIFE OF BATH
4 Upper Bridge St, Wye, Ashford (01233) 812540

1

This is where le tout Ashford gets togged up to go out on Saturday nights. The house is not unattractive; the dining room looks sumptuous, feels plush. Wines are well-chosen, cosmopolitan. The trouble is the cooking – which is dire. Now and then comes an item which is passable, but most of the stuff is nasty and some of it is truly horrible: lamb with laven-der and rosemary tastes of lavatory cleaner; fried mushrooms would disgrace a Little Chef.

L AND D TUES TO SAT £75

OXFORDSHIRE

15 NORTH PARADE
15 North Parade Ave, Oxford (01865) 513773

5

Ambitious bistro with variable but mostly sound cooking. Well made sauces, such as port and calvados, go with guinea fowl and game; the ice creams and sorbets are fine; the wine list is only moderately marked up but fails to include much of interest at the lower end.

L AND D EVERY DAY £60

THE BOATHOUSE
The Beetle and Wedge Hotel, Ferry Lane, Moulsford-on-Thames (01491) 651381

7

A rather ramshackle group of buildings beside the river and attached to a modest hotel (which has its own, posher, restau-rant under the same ownership). The cooking owes much to the tradition of Elizabeth David and to considered bistro practice. It is unerringly expert. Banal-sounding things such as duck terrine are first rate, rabbit sauté with lardons is unbeliev-ably rich and delicious; the ham is as fine as you'll come across in Britain. Puds are good and the service is charming.

L AND D EVERY DAY £80

DEXTER'S
4
Market Place, Deddington (01869) 338813

The ironstone buildings glower like a choleric redhead; if
Paul Johnson was a village near Banbury, he'd be Deddington.
Dexters looks out to a grand church and a humble town hall.
The interior is cottagey, haphazard. The chef is in thrall to
English mustard. He comes on like a missionary from Carrow.
It is used to dress a salad alongside a foie gras terrine, then
turns up, more succesfully, in mashed potato with pork and
leek sausages – ample mustard is served on the side. Bread
and butter pudding comes with nutmeg custard, not mustard.
The service is far from speedy.

L AND D TUES TO SAT £60+

THE FEATHERS HOTEL
8
Market St, Woodstock (01993) 812291

Where it previously offered great grub at more or less everyday
prices, it has stepped up a couple of gears and now whacks
you with turbo-assisted gastronomy and a tab to match.
Recommended: excellently melting pasta with scallops, truffles
and truffle oil; outstanding risotto with langoustines, rocket
and a delightful emulsion of raw tomato and olive oil; foie gras
fried with chunks of guinea fowl. Cheeses from Paxton and
Whitfield are misspelled but properly chosen.

L AND D EVERY DAY £95+

LE MANOIR AUX QUAT' SAISONS
10
Church Rd, Great Milton (01844) 278881

Quite phenomenal cooking by Raymond Blanc in dreamlike
surroundings. Blanc has little in common with any other chef
and may be counted a miraculous freak: although he was born
in France, he never worked in a kitchen there and has lived
more than half his life in this country. His amazing culinary
creations include: pasta with foie gras and cabbage and truffles; duck ham with duck tripe candied in truffle oil; beef with
bone marrow and horseradish crust and an Hermitage sauce;
a millefeuille of foie gras with potatoes and turnips. Along with
Fernet Branca, sex and Dungeness, everyone should
experience it once.

L AND D EVERY DAY £240, SET LUNCH £110

THE SIR CHARLES NAPIER RESTAURANT 7
Sprigg's Alley, Chinnor (exit 6 on M40) (01494) 483011

Amiably eccentric outfit on the western escarpment of the Chilterns. The furnishings are junk shop trove, Dada jokes, etc. There is a formidable cellar. The chef delivers precisely judged dishes which are presented with a pleasing austerity; the ingredients are allowed to speak for themselves. Recommended: lamb saddle with gratin dauphinois; goat cheese and red pepper tart; grilled salmon with ratatouille vegetables; black pudding and bacon salad. There are decent British and Irish cheeses. Sculptures are exhibited in the gardens. A genuinely congenial and enjoyable place.

L TUES TO SUN, D TUES TO SAT £75+, SET LUNCH £45

SURREY

THE CLOISTERS 2
The Nutfield Priory Hotel Nutfield, Redhill
(01737) 822066

Barracks-like Victorian Gothic hotel on the Wealden escarpment. Looks like a loony bin, and certain of the staff behave as though they're already working in one. Still, the over-wrought wood and heraldically coloured organ in the hall are all gruesomely attractive, and the perpendicular stone corridor that houses the restaurant is not to be forgotten. By the standards of also-ran country-house hotels, the cooking is good. The chef will doubtless make his name elsewhere. Here, he makes mistakes, as well as scoring some real hits. Duck breast with duck leg done in caul fat is good; risotto is sound, even if not quite what's advertised; rabbit saddle is almost there. A twice-baked soufflé is all albumen, a savoury meringue; a bumptiously annotated wine list includes bargains and oddities.

L SUN TO FRI, D EVERY DAY £75+

KINGHAM'S 7
Gomshall Lane, Shere, Guildford (01483) 202168

Situated in a village of near-emetic cuteness, the restaurant (beams, sabres, copper pans) is very cosy. The chef, Paul Baker, has a real feel for what he cooks. He is not scared to do simple things: grilled Dover sole with lime butter was just right, and so was the creamy mashed potato with it. Wild mushroom soup was first-rate: deeply flavoured, bosky, not over-refined. Full marks for crisply roasted potatoes, and also for the service.

L TUES TO SUN, D TUES TO SAT £60 (SET LUNCH £42+)

MICHEL'S

4

Ripley High St, Ripley (01483) 224777

Good-looking, airy restaurant in the middle of a
quintessentially Surrey village. The cooking suffers the
all-too often encountered Home Counties failing of putting
presentation before flavour. Nonetheless, not a bad place and
one which might become rather impressive, were the kitchen
to let itself go a bit. Aromatic rabbit salad; bland lamb with
wimpish tarragon mousse, smoked salmon with blinis. Decent
wines at decent prices and congenial service.

L SUN, D TUES TO SAT £70

PARTNERS

6

2-4 West St, Dorking (01306) 882826

Smoothly-run dining rooms on two floors. Very sound cooking,
if tending to over-richness: cod with a herb crust and a butter
sauce; haddock soufflé with haddock soup; pork fillet with
potato and mushroom gratin. Well-made puddings in a lighter
vein. Amiable wines.

L TUES TO FRI, D TUES TO SAT £60+ AT LUNCHTIME,
DINNER IS MORE

SUPERFISH

3

9 Castle Parade, Bypass Rd, Ewell, Epsom (020) 8393 3674

This is a clean and greaseless chippie, where you are given a
complementary plate of prawns, which may be followed by any
one of about 8 fish in decent batter. The service is cheery and
the chips OK. There are a couple of branches nearby.

L AND D MON TO SAT £8-£20

SUSSEX

5

ALEXANDER HOUSE

East St, Turners Hill West (01342) 714914

Rather magnificently appointed 'country-house' hotel with
good paintings and fine gewgaws. Some of the cooking is
commonplace luxury, some of it is inventive and in an idiom
rarely found in such establishments: omelette with girolles,
delicious venison with fruits. Indifferent wines, no smoking.

L AND D EVERY DAY £120

ANGEL HOTEL   6
North St, Midhurst (01730) 812421

One of the few worthwhile smalltown hotels. It is properly
run, relaxed, eager to please. There are good and unusual
wines and Gale's beers from down the road. The kitchen
eschews gimmicks and fantasy. It buys well, and balances
refinement and earthiness to a T. Deep-fried squid with aioli,
or with scallops and their coral; fine roast pork with separately
crisped crackling and sweet paprika sauce; venison with port
sauce; beef with mushroom sauce. Everything is characterised
by diligence, perfect timing and total care.

L AND D EVERY DAY £70+

THE BLACK CHAPATI   7
12 Circus Parade, New England Rd, Brighton
(01273) 699011

A one-off, whose menu comprises a number of subcontinental
dishes. The straightforward items are done with flair and
without resort to Indian catering practices; the others are
highly original. Among the best items are lamb rack with a
spiced crust; creamed potatoes spiked with chillis; king prawns
with spicy pickled onions. Ordinary items, such as rice and
(of course) chapatis, are raised to real heights.

D TUES TO SAT £50+

THE BRAZZ   4
Upper Level, Enterprise Centre, Eastbourne
(01323) 643889

Slow service hides surprisingly good cooking: field mushrooms
stewed in garlicky cream, calf's liver with bacon and shallots.

L MON TO SAT, D WED TO SAT £40

CHINA GARDEN   3
88 Preston St, Brighton (01273) 325124

Wouldn't make a big noise in Soho, but a useful address
nonetheless. The range of dim sum is not particularly wide
– 30 items, say – but the quality is unexceptionable. Steamed
dishes are superior to those which are deep-fried with a heavy
hand. Cheung fun are well made.

L AND D EVERY DAY £50

GARDEN RESTAURANT   6
Gatwick Hilton, Gatwick Airport (01293) 518080

A Hilton airport hotel with a serious restaurant. Good cooking:
noodles with sweetbreads, chicken and basil; grouse with
celeriac puree; pungent Burgundian cheeses.

L AND D EVERY DAY £80

JOLLY SPORTSMAN

7

Chapel Lane, East Chiltington, Lewes (01273) 890400

Amiable, relaxed, and notably unhushed. It is not the most beautiful of buildings and it's fair to say that it has been fitted out on shoestring. But so what? The cooking is robust, savoury, skilled, unpretentious. Smoked haddock is well done in a buttery feuillette; both steak and rare tuna are served with a sort of potato cake and are nicely sauced. Choucroute with duck confit, ham and three sorts of sausage is first-rate. There's a good selection of beers and decent wines at ungrabby prices.

L TUES TO SUN, D TUES TO SAT £55+

LANDGATE BISTRO

5

5/6 Landgate, Rye (01797) 222829

Pleasant and unfussy, and thus rather unexpected among the tea-shoppes of Olde Rye. The cooking is simple, unaffected French bourgeois. Fish stew with world-class aioli, duck with lime sauce, lamb with tomato and basil sauce. Well-chosen cheap wines.

D TUES TO SAT £60+

LYCHGATES

6

5a Church St, Old Town, Bexhill-on-Sea (01424) 212193

Small and homely restaurant serving well-judged, understated food. Impressive starters, delicious puds, amiable service. Now has a website: www.leet.co.uk.

D WED TO SAT £60

THE MERMAID RESTAURANT

4

2 Rock-a-Nore, Hastings (01424) 438100

The best site. Sit outside and you get the strangest buildings in England – the net huts and the fishing boats which occasioned them. Fish and chips is all that's on offer, and it's ace. Ace fish, ace batter, ace timing, ace skill. The resultant fish is crisp, grease-less, briney.

7.30AM–7.30PM WED TO SUN, 7.30AM–3PM MON AND TUES £15

ONE PASTON PLACE

8

1 Paston Pl, Brighton (01273) 606933

Chef Mark Emmerson has blossomed into a most estimable craftsman. His dishes are impeccable French, gently, yet deeply flavoured, excellently judged. This is real cooking and it owns the confidence not to require embellishment. A pungent and light pissaladière was about as good as this Niçoise version of the pizza can get; foie gras with fig was as good as it was unusual.

L AND D TUES TO SAT £100

SOUTH WEST

BRISTOL

HOTEL DU VIN & BISTRO

9

The Sugar House, Narrow Lewins Mead, Bristol
(01179) 255577

A startlingly inventive reclamation of two adjoining buildings
that were derelict for going on 20 years – a convincing Queen
Anne pastiche and a sturdy early 19th-century refinery. The
restaurant, like those of its siblings in Tunbridge Wells and
Winchester, is woody, parchment-coloured, hung with
wine-related posters. Cooking is robust and wholesome: crab
croquettes with an uncooked tomato sauce; a potato cake with
marinated anchovies; lightly battered scallops; rabbit with a
classic mustard sauce. The cheeses couldn't be bettered.

L AND D EVERY DAY £65

MARKWICKS

10

43 Corn St, Bristol (01179) 262658

Stephen Markwick conjures luxury from humble ingredients.
Lamb's breads are cooked with strips of pasta and marsala
sauce. Calf's offal is dusted with fine crumb, fried and served
with sherry cream. The charcuterie is impeccable. Guinea fowl
is served with pommes Anna cooked with duck fat; bourride is
spiced with aniseed, cumin and garlic. This is one of the most
consistently pleasing restaurants in Britain, one of the greats.

L MON TO FRI, D MON TO SAT £85 (SET MENUS LESS)

CORNWALL

HOTEL TRESANTON

8

27 Lower Castle Rd, St Mawes (01326) 270055

A white roughcast house of the Thirties, which has been
comprehensively made over with absolute sureness of taste
by its new owner, Olga Polizzi. There is abundant tongue-and-
groove, good seascapes, engaging lumps of sculpture. The
cooking is polished and restrained using not just fish, but
locally reared meat, locally grown vegetables. The wines are
ones that you want to drink.

L AND D EVERY DAY £65+

PORTHMINSTER BEACH RESTAURANT 5
Porthminster Beach, St Ives (01736) 795352
The dining room looks across the bay and toward the harbour;
the staff are enthusiastically congenial and the cooking is
commendable in its straightforward treatment of fresh
ingredients: grilled sardines with onions and rosemary,
mackerel with a truly excellent lemon pickle.

L AND D EVERY DAY £38+

THE SEAFOOD RESTAURANT 9
Riverside, Padstow (01841) 532700
Big, busy, polished quayside place that seems improbably
sophisticated for north Cornwall. The cooking makes no
concession to provincial taste. Rick Stein is an audacious original
who has the combination of confidence, technique and
imagination to make up his own rules. A vast mix of shellfish is
heated rather than cooked and served with a dressing of
perfumed oil, chilli, garlic and parsley. He is also capable of
combining the Asiatic and the Italian without making a balls-up –
e.g., bass with salsa verde, a coriander and chilli relish and
capillary noodles. Intensely flavoured roasted red peppers are used
as a 'sauce' for monkfish; fish soup is more aggressively flavoured
than most of the food. The main characteristic is douceur.

L AND D EVERY DAY £100+

ST PETROC'S BISTRO 6
4 New St, Padstow (01841) 532700
The little sister of the seafood restaurant down the road.
Hunky telly idol Rick Stein merely supervises. Oeufs en
meurette is well made. Pork sausages from a farm near St
Austell are good. And the fish soup just about out-does
Stein's own. Maybe it is Stein's own. The customers in
summer tend to be loudmouthed city people from Rock,
the Fulham-by-Sea across the estuary.

L AND D TUES TO SUN £85

DORSET

THE CASTLEMAN HOTEL 4
Chettle, Blandford Forum (01258) 830096
The big house at Chettle is baroque, by Archer. The hotel
occupies the former dower house – part Georgian, part 1830s
Tudor. Lack of fuss is almost an article of faith. The kitchen is
fastidious, vaguely worthy. Lack of elaboration doesn't always
come off, and seasonings can be approximate.

L SUN, D EVERY DAY £50

LA FLEUR DE LYS

2

25 Salisbury St, Shaftesbury (01747) 853717

The decorative style is unprovincial. The style of cooking is –
not altogether surprisingly – elaborate. Sculpted apples with
cheese (and not a single local cheese among them); raspberry
garnishing pigeon breast; cooked camembert with smoked
chicken. There is an abundance of stuffing and of sweet sauce.
Good bread, good wines.

L TUES TO SUN, D MON TO SAT (CLOSED MONDAYS IN WINTER) £70

THE LANGTON ARMS

1

Tarrant Monkton, Blandford Forum (01258) 830225

Long, low pub beneath Crichel Down. It gets packed out, a
reflection of the lack of local competition, no doubt. Good
ingredients are not well served by approximate cooking: pheasant is desiccated, though still well flavoured; crab is mugged by
cheese, though still nicely fresh. Good beers include the pub's
'own' brew from Smiles of Bristol and others from Batemans,
Fullers, etc. Treacle tart is a treat.

L AND D EVERY DAY £55

THE MUSEUM HOTEL

2

Farnham, Blandford Forum (01725) 516261

The titular museum itself – the Pitt Rivers – has been extinct
for getting on for 30 years. But that martial archaeologist's
vaguely pagan park, the Larmer Tree Grounds, is one of the
most delightful anomalies of southern England. This pub is
just down the road.

L AND D EVERY DAY £80

RIVERSIDE RESTAURANT

7

West Bay, Bridport (01308) 422011

Unpretentious, canteen-like, though not without ambition.
Grilled mackerel, skate with black butter and, in another vein,
jellied eels are splendid. When the cooking gets fancier, the
results are not quite so certain, however. The selection of
wines is impressive and sensibly concentrates on that which
is drinkable and affordable.

L TUES TO SUN, D TUES TO SAT (CLOSED BETWEEN DECEMBER
AND EARLY FEBRUARY) £50+

SHELL BAY SEAFOOD RESTAURANT 3
Ferry Rd, Studland (01929) 450363
Close by the Sandbanks to Studland ferry and with a great
aspect of Poole harbour. The premises are a 1950s bungalow,
which is abundantly glazed. The kitchen's weak point is its
neglect to peel things. Some of the fish is inventively
butchered – a plaice is cut across its width and is far from
insipid.

L AND D EVERY DAY FROM 1 APRIL TO 1 OCTOBER; L THURS TO
SUN, D THURS TO SAT, OCT TO MARCH (CLOSED JANUARY) £50

STOCK HILL 3
Wyke, Gillingham (01747) 823626
If ornament was, as the Austrian architect Adolf Loos stated,
crime, then his compatriots who run this mid-Victorian hotel
would be doing life. It takes over-decoration to unprecedented
heights. Pharaonic kitsch is a strong suit, but then so are
bronzes and Venetian mirrors, and Aryan statuary and
chocolate box paintings. The aggregate is both saccharine and
sinister. Cooking is relentlessly sweet-toothed – as though one
half only of the pan-Germanic sweet and sour prescription has
been adhered to. This tendency applies also to the wines.

L TUES TO THURS AND SUN, D EVERY DAY £90

SUMMER LODGE 3
Evershot (01935) 83424
Full-dress country-house hotel between Dorchester and Yeovil.
Formal, moderately chintzy, courteously run, full of people
talking in whispers. The cooking is witlessly elaborate: butter
is moulded into the shape of a tomato and given a real tomato
stem; steamed potatoes are sculpted into perfect ovals.
Puddings are good. But a patissier's fussy hand does not work
in meat cookery and the concentration on peripheral fripperies
is generally at the cost of resolved dishes.

L AND D EVERY DAY £95+

GLOUCESTERSHIRE

LE CHAMPIGNON SAUVAGE

7

24-26 Suffolk Rd, Cheltenham (01242) 573449

Simple decor, far from simple cooking; indeed, by provincial standards this is a singularly adventurous outfit. Over-elaboration does creep in here and there, but the majority of dishes are sound and some are exciting. Tripe is braised with pig's trotter, and is as good as you will get in Britain. Fillet of cod is served with pea puree, pigeon with black pudding. There are numerous vinous bargains.

L AND D TUES TO SAT: SET LUNCH £45, SET DINNER £60+

LE PETIT BLANC

3

The Queens Hotel, The Promenade, Cheltenham
(01242) 266800

The premises are modern – zinc tables, brown leather banquettes, a continuous cornice fresco. A smoked haddock and rice confection was a savoury rice pudding with a glaze of sorrel sabayon and parmesan shavings. A chocolate tart with marscapone ice cream was excellent, of the standard one might expect of an outfit connected, however tenuously, with Le Manoir aux Quat' Saisons. With luck, the insipid sausages have been replaced.

L AND D EVERY DAY £75+

SOMERSET

BABINGTON HOUSE

8

Babington, Frome (01373) 812266

The country branch of the London club called Soho House is approached up a dead-straight avenue of a certain magnificence. The house looks Georgian, but Pevsner says c.1700. Expansively generous flavours and country dishes done with real élan. Baked field mushrooms with garlic butter were delicious; mussels were done with garlic and parsley, tuna with fried potatoes. Best of all was boeuf bourguignon that had been long marinated in decent wine. The staff are amiable and willing.

L AND D EVERY DAY £80

BRAZZ

7

Castle Bow, Taunton (01823) 252000

Kit Chapman, the owner of the adjacent Castle Hotel has created a restaurant/bar/cafe of real excellence. The design is quasi-modern: an all-glass front with a hyperbolic B as the door handle, a stainless steel bar. It is not so refined as the Castle's cooking, but when you get a top-grade craftsman knocking out supposedly everyday gear you still end up with something special.

L AND D EVERY DAY £50+

THE CASTLE

10

Castle Green, Taunton (01823) 272671

A very fine outfit indeed – the bastion of top-notch, intelligent English cooking. Potted duck has kinship with both rillettes and liver pâté; excellent crab tart; braised lamb is flavoured with garlic and thyme. Chapman is one of this country's top hoteliers. He knows it's all in the details. Great wines.

L EVERY DAY, D MON TO SAT £100

HOMEWOOD PARK

7

Hinton Charterhouse, near Bath (01225) 723731

The friendliest and most comforting of 'country-house' hotels. The early Victorian building overlooks the Avon valley. The staff is remarkable and the cooking is of real distinction. Substantial dishes are given a light touch and the results are commendable. Lightly smoked haddock is done with lentils that have been cooked with bacon; lamb is given a hazelnut crust and is served with a potato and cream gratin so unctuously delicious it deserves to be a course on its own. The wines are impressive.

L AND D EVERY DAY £80 PLUS

THE OLIVE TREE

8

The Queensberry Hotel, Russell St, Bath (01225) 447928

Absolutely reliable, totally congenial – this is the basement of the Queensberry Hotel, which is the best place to stay in Bath. Delicious peculiarities might include duck with plums and ginger, chicken with a soupy couscous, spiced lamb. Good wines.

L MON TO SAT, D EVERY DAY £70+

WILTSHIRE

BISHOPSTROW HOUSE

8

Boreham Rd, Warminster (01985) 212312

A harsh stone Regency lump whose inside has been decorated with muscular brio and a total disregard for convention. The grounds are excellent: a tunnel leads beneath the main road to a secret garden beside the Wylye – here there are cedars, wellingtonias, two Georgian temples and a walled orchard. The kitchen delivers a succession of technically deft and flavoursome dishes with a refined rural accent: potted rabbit with pickled pear; lightly smoked pork with swede and shallots; lamb shank with top-notch mash. Also impressive in a different vein: seared tuna with turnips, olives and carrots and pungent oil; almost perfumed duck confit with potato salad; chocolate sponge with a liquid chocolate filling. This is among the most relaxed of country-house hotels.

L AND D EVERY DAY £80

THE COMPASSES

2

Chicksgrove, Tisbury (01722) 714318

Chilmark stone pub in the Nadder valley west of Salisbury.
There's not a burr to be heard, received pronunciation rules.
The cooking is variable – chicken liver pâté is underseasoned
roughage; but venison stroganoff is splendid. The coffee is filth
from a cafetière, but the beer is Wadworth's.

L TUES TO SUN, D TUES TO SAT £50

THE GEORGE AND DRAGON

6

High St, Rowde, nr Devizes (01380) 723053

The menu is overlong, but when things go right the results
are pleasing. Most fish dishes are reliable, and so too, the
egg dishes, such as smoked salmon tart.

L AND D TUES TO SAT £55+

HARPER'S

2

6-7 Ox Row, Market Sq, Salisbury (01722) 333118

Fairly simple first floor restaurant overlooking Salisbury's
impressive market place. Good rack of lamb; mushroom tart;
attentively prepared vegetables; impressive selection of French
regional wines.

L MON TO SAT, D EVERY DAY IN SUMMER, CLOSE SUN
& REST OF YEAR £40

HOWARD'S HOUSE HOTEL

5

Teffont Evias, Salisbury (01722) 716392

The village is a dream of the picturesque: steeply wooded hills,
parkland, a lake, a surprisingly grand church and a romantically
castellated manor house. The hotel occupies the former dower
house. It is a delightful place. Mullet is served with rhubarb; veal
rump is perfectly roasted. The French wines are well chosen and
ungreedily marked up. Good cheeses and delicious puddings.

L SUN, D EVERY DAY £75+

JADE RESTAURANT

3

109a Exeter St, Salisbury (01722) 333355

Cantonese fish den, whose simpler dishes are better than
those involving batter. The customers are yobbish, the waiters
long-suffering.

L AND D MON TO SAT £45

LES MIRABELLES

7

Forest Row, Nomansland, Salisbury, Wiltshire SB5
(01794) 390205
Improbably chintzy joint in a former shack colony on the
very boundary of the New Forest. It is totally French. The chef presumably comes from somewhere like Nancy – the eastern accent
is unmistakable in such things as a warm pork pâté in pastry, or in
mammarial pieces of quail and foie gras. Scallops are done with a
butter sauce, rabbit is done with mustard. Puddings are well made.
The wine list includes a number of oddities from Lorraine.

L TUE TO SUN, D TUE TO SAT £60

THE SILVER PLOUGH

1

White Hill, Pitton, Salisbury, Wiltshire SP5 (01722) 712266
Twee pub in a downland declivity. It's the sort of place that
serves 'wine' made from damsons or rhubarb. The cooking is
dismally hick; styrofoam Yorkshire pudding; swede mugged by
hallucinatory doses of nutmeg; overcooked salmon with an
inept tomato and ginger sauce. One wonders if the chef actually tastes any of this stuff. If so, he or she has a wobbly palate.

L AND D EVERY DAY £60

WOOLLEY GRANGE

4

Woolley Green, Bradford-on-Avon (01225) 864705
Good-looking Jacobean and early Victorian limestone hotel.
Unusually for a 'country-house' joint, it welcomes children.
The cooking is, however, for adults. It's sophisticated, generally
unfussy, surehanded. Turbot and scallops with a squid ink sauce
and dark grey pasta is as good to taste as it is to look at; chicken
and guinea fowl are gently and impressively sauced. The vegetables tend to be on the foetal side but are, in compensation,
served in copious quantities. Good puddings, poorly thought-out
wine list with very little to drink under about £18.

L AND D EVERY DAY £100

MIDLANDS

HEREFORDSHIRE

THE RIVERSIDE INN

6

Aymestrey (01568) 708440

André Cluzeau is a gutsy kind of cook. Chicken liver parfait
was first-rate. Top-notch beef was served with a tarragon
sauce. Duck confit was of a similar rate. Venison was hugely
impressive: the meat was perfectly hung and deftly cooked.
The beers, with avian names, are home-brewed.

L AND D EVERY DAY £60+

THE STAGG INN

8

**Titley, Kington (on the B4355, 8 miles NW of
Leominster)** (01544) 230221

This is much more the kind of place one is likely to come
upon in boondocks France than in England: unpretentious,
lively, amiably run and doggedly regional. Steve Reynolds is
a splendid cook. He has fine local ingredients and he knows
what to do with them. Boned quail is stuffed with the lightest
and most savoury of forcemeats; local, free-range pork is
gamey, sweet and tender with just a hint of kidney flavour.
Fine beef is done with an equally fine roesti. Cheeses come
from within 40 or so miles and are offered in peak condition.

L AND D TUES TO SUN £60+

LINCOLNSHIRE

THE GEORGE

2

St Martin's, Stamford (01780) 750750

Much of the cooking is insipid and ill-judged, but this good-
looking hotel, in one of the finest small towns in England, is
a good place to stay and drink in.

L AND D EVERY DAY £60+

WIG AND MITRE

4

30-32 Steep Hill, Lincoln (01522) 535190

A pub and cafe as well as a restaurant. The last occupies
the former hall of the medieval house. Impressive structural
beams. Unimpressive tea-shoppe decor. Service is amateurish.
The kitchen is erratic. A twice-baked cheese soufflé was good
and cod chowder was passable. Confit of chicken was nothing
to do with confit, but, rather, was overdone roast fowl.

L AND D EVERY DAY £65

WINTERINGHAM FIELDS 9
Winteringham, near Scunthorpe (01724) 733096
A 16th-century house full of Victorian gewgaws and furniture
overlooking the Humber. The young staff is sound. The cooking, by the Swiss owner-chef, is unusual, often elaborate and
almost consistently successful. Impressive cheeses and some
good wines, including a number of Swiss bottles.

L AND D TUES TO SAT £110+, SET LUNCH £65, ROOMS FROM £70

NORTHAMPTONSHIRE

THE ROADHOUSE RESTAURANT 7
16 High St, Roade, Northampton (01604) 863372
Gutsy cooking, strong on game – a useful place in a
gastronomically barren part of England. Attentive service,
decent cheap wines, serious cheeses.

L MON TO FRI AND SUN, D MON TO SAT £70

VINE HOUSE 7
100 High St, Paulerspury (01327) 811267
Old stone farmhouse between Milton Keynes and Towcester.
Some of the cooking is very good indeed: rabbit soup with
leeks and lentils; potted oxtail wrapped in cabbbage leaves;
saffron ice cream. But duck confit is spoiled by a cloying sweet
apricot chutney and turbot gains nothing from sweated peppers
and onions. Perhaps the only restaurant in England that makes
its own ginger beer.

L WED TO FRI, D MON TO SAT £70

NOTTINGHAMSHIRE

HART'S 6
Park Row, Nottingham (0115) 911 0666
The premises were converted from a wing of the former general
hospital on the edge of the singular 19th-century development
called The Park. The result is a notably cheering and welcom-
ing room, one which is tended by an aptly smiley staff and
served by a kitchen which delivers with startling alacrity. The
cooking, which shows real polish, is also occasionally bizarre in
appearance. Two first courses, which seemed to have been
fashioned after Dutch caps, were actually domes of deep-fried
pasta filled with goat cheese and black pudding. Main courses
include reworked classics: cassoulet was perverse but satisfying.

L AND D EVERY DAY £60, SET LUNCH £40

SONNY'S   4
3 Carlton St, Nottingham (0115) 947 3041
Converted shop in the lace market area of the city. The menu
comprises new British standards – i.e., it is eclectic and most
dishes are multi-partite. Everything comes with something
else, not necessarily something that is complementary. Steak
with lemon thyme butter (and very good chips); potato
pancake with salmon eggs.

L AND D EVERY DAY £70+

RUTLAND

HAMBLETON HALL   8
Hambleton, Oakham (01572) 756991
The house is a confident essay in the Old English style of
the late 1870s. Views across Rutland Water are extensive.
The cooking is elaborate, but it is also splendidly balanced –
nothing is redundant. Recommended: lobster tortellini with
vegetable 'spaghetti'; wild mushroom tart with foie gras and
sweetbreads; bass with an aubergine fritter and red pepper
sauce; pigeon with a poached ravioli of foie gras; a gratin of
rhubarb and strawberries with fromage blanc ice cream. The
wine list is strong on bordeaux and burgundy; the staff are
perky and civil.

L AND D EVERY DAY £120

SHROPSHIRE

COUNTRY FRIENDS   6
Dorrington, Shrewsbury (01743) 718707
A much restored black-and-white house just north of the Long
Mynd. The dining room is just the job if you like pink velvet
with everything. Cooking is variable but at its best hits real
heights: duck with sauternes, fried cauliflower, halibut with
chive sauce.

L WED TO SAT, D TUES TO SAT £60+

GOLDSTONE HALL   6
**Near Market Drayton (turn east off the A529 between
Newport and Market Drayton at Hinstock)**
(01630) 661202
The hotel dining room is Thirties Tudor. Despite being in the
middle of nowhere, the feel is of a genteel suburban tea-room.
The chef is original and spirited, although he does make
howlers – e.g., serving sorbets between courses and attempting
to cook beef Wellington. But his hefty, savoury compilations,
such as a fricassee of his own wild boar sausages, wild boar

faggots and lamb's kidneys in a mustard and tarragon sauce, are great. Rabbit with ceps and cream is in a similar vein. The puddings are trad English. The wines are disappointing; cheeses are exemplary.

L AND D EVERY DAY £75+

THE MERCHANT HOUSE

9

Lower Corve St, Ludlow (01584) 875438

England's finest small-town restaurant. It is all beams and colourwash outside and all beams and idiosyncrasy within: Indian tapestries, potent paintings, non-airport lumps of African sculpture, etc. Shaun Hill's cooking is admirably low-tech, sharp, neat, bright. Sweetbreads plainly done with kidney and a potato cake with shards of olive in it are delicious. Hare is roasted, and light. Veal is delicately sauced with mustard. Cheeses and wines from superlative sources.

L FRI AND SAT, D TUES TO SAT £78, LESS AT LUNCH

STAFFORDSHIRE

OLD BEAMS

6

Bleak Rd, Waterhouses (01538) 308254

A genuinely charming joint run by a family who take an evident pride in their business. Father cooks confidently, precisely; mother and son run the restaurant with unforced amiability. 'Capriccio' of pigeon was raw in the manner of carpaccio; the leg beside it was cooked – an unusual and successful dish. Chargrilled lamb fillet was singularly succulent. The rooms are a steal by British standards.

L FRI AND SUN, D TUES TO SAT £100

WARWICKSHIRE

BOSQUET

5

97a Warwick Rd, Kenilworth (01926) 852463

Chintzy, intimate, front parlourish place. Excellent petits vins – all French – and kindredly monoglot cooking, whose execution is not always as precise as it might be. A croustade of pigeon and chestnuts is marred by overcooked meat and lifted by a masterly port sauce; venison is cooked too rare; beef fillet is exemplary. Desserts are numbingly sweet.

L TUES TO FRI, D TUES TO SAT £90+

NUTHURST GRANGE

2

Hockley Heath (01564) 783972

Country-house hotel between Brum and Stratford. The
cooking is relentlessly dainty, dinky, cutesy. Excellent sweets.

L SUN TO FRI, D EVERY DAY £110

SIMPSONS

4

101-103 Warwick Rd, Kenilworth (01926) 864567

Dishes from all over the world crop up in a maze of cream and
green rooms. Spring rolls from China, gravlax from Abba, pastilla
from Morocco, foie gras from France, and so on. Puddings are
not bad at all. The wines are similarly cosmopolitan.

L AND D TUES TO SAT £90+

WEST MIDLANDS

ADIL

3

148-150 Stoney Lane, Sparkbrook (0121) 449 0335

A basic and excellent cafe specialising in 'balti'. Dishes
are served in wok-like vessels called 'karahi'. The range of
vegetables is extensive and there are also finely spiced meat,
poultry and pulse compositions.

L AND D EVERY DAY £12+

LOS AMIGOS

2

806 Bristol Rd, Selly Oak, Birmingham (0121) 471 3577

Small South American diner with dishes from all over the
subcontinent. The live music is a bore but some of the dishes
are all right, if rather crude: hot beef stew, hot lamb stew,
empanadas stuffed with chicken or beef and raisins, chicken
with cream sauce. Mexican beer is a better bet than the rather
dismal selection of wines.

D TUES TO SAT £28+

CHUNG YING

1

16 Wrottesley St, Birmingham (0121) 622 5669

The premises are apparently undecorated in years, with cooking to match. Roast meats – duck and pork – were OK, but
the composed dishes were bereft of zip. And the duck meat in
a stir-fry tasted unforgiveably stale.

L AND D EVERY DAY £30+

CHUNG YING GARDEN

4

17 Thorpe St, Birmingham (0121) 666 6622

Mecca for devotees of offal and oddities in Brum's Chinatown:
deep-fried pig's intestines; duck webs; fish lips; tongues of fowl.

L AND D EVERY DAY £45+

HOTEL DU VIN & BISTRO   8
25 Church St, Birmingham (0121) 236 0559

The former Birmingham and Midland Eye Hospital has
been boldly remade: a strong, sombre palette is everywhere
apparent. There are Venetian mirrors, paintings of magnified
crustacea, Adamish panels, a startling range of malts, ditto
cigars. The menu features simple dishes which are properly
prepared. Salt beef with an English mustard dressing and
garlicky mash was the biz, as were sweet lamb chump and
roesti, bloody roast beef and crisply roast rare salmon. There
is a plethora of good wines at low prices.

L AND D EVERY DAY £75

JONATHAN'S   1
16-20 Wolverhampton Rd, Oldbury (0121) 429 3757

The ne plus ultra of the 'traditional' English restaurant. Olde?
Verye. It occupies most of a Thirties shopping parade. The
shops have been gutted and replaced by a crazy maze that
beggars description – Morris wallpaper, pub signs, lincrusta,
ancient typewriters, hideous teapots. The menu descriptions
are, of course, crass and pretentious. Cooking is mostly lacklustre. There's quite a decent smoked fish tart, though, and
gooseberry water-ice is all right.

L SUN TO FRI, D EVERY DAY £70

LANGTRY'S, MARRIOT HOTEL   5
12 Hagley Rd, Birmingham (0121) 452 1144

It's nothing special to look at: architectural prints, Lloyd Loom
chairs, floral curtains. The cooking is miles better than one has
come to expect of chain hotels: it is almost unnecessarily good.
Lamb's kidneys with strips of smoked bacon, button onions
and a light renal gravy was about as good a rendition of that
dish as is possible. Duck confit had skin as crisp as crackling
and the meat was potent. The service is friendly.

L MON TO SAT, D EVERY DAY £70+

OCEANIC   4
89 Livery St, Birmingham (0121) 236 7500

Not a place to face sober. The walls of this big semi-basement are
cobalt going on royal; the lights are pachyderms' condoms. Chairs
are crimson and so are the sconces, to each of which is attached a
vial bearing a marigold. Crab and gruyère tart is a moulded fish
cake on an iffy pastry base; salmon with chilli was precisely cooked
– but not helped by underdone courgettes, unpeeled potatoes and
boiled tomatoes. The staff are unfazed by any demand.

L MON TO FRI, D MON TO SAT £65+

LE PETIT BLANC 3
9 Brindleyplace, Birmingham (0121) 633 7333
Judged alongside other chain restaurants, it seems a moderately
classy act. The place is unquestionably handsome – all hard
dges and whiteness and cantilevered stairs. The cooking is
unremarkable: gazpacho was undersalted, while crab cakes were
a forlorn attempt to rustle up a spot of Thai cooking. Indifferent
Toulouse sausages were served with so-so mash and greasy onions.
As for the bread – just because it has raisins in it, doesn't mean
that it shouldn't be fresh.

L AND D EVERY DAY £75+

RESTAURANT GILMORE 5
27 Warstone Lane, Birmingham (0121) 233 3655
The premises are entered by a tiled corridor and a flowery yard.
The room is long and narrow with lots of tough red brick and
structural girders. Walls are hung with such ill-advised
decorations as flying ducks. Paul Gilmore can certainly cook,
however. Smoked haddock was done with smoked bacon and a
light, smooth and delicious potato puree. A curiously perfumed
tapenade accompanied mullet fillets, sauce vierge and roast
tomatoes: the centrepiece was excellent. Tournedos was properly
hung and abundantly flavoured. Desserts were well up to scratch.

L TUES TO FRI, D TUES TO SAT £60

SAN CARLO 1
4 Temple St, Birmingham (0121) 633 0251
The menu recalls the bad old days of Britalian restauration.
Flat pasta with lobster are served with the empty half shell of
the crustacean. Rigatoni were sauced with tomato and portion-
controlled sausage.

L AND D EVERY DAY £50+

WING WAH 5
**Unit 1a, Wing Yip Central, Thimble Mill Lane,
Nechells, Birmingham** (0121) 327 7879
The football-stadium sized restaurant north of the epic Wing Yip
warehouses. There are five hundred-odd items. Chicken with
Chinese ham and bok choi was rich, soothing. Turbot, flash-fried
then braised with soy sauce and garlic, was impressive.

11AM–11PM MON TO SAT, 11AM–10PM SUN £40+

WORCESTERSHIRE

BROCKENCOTE HALL 4
Chaddesley Corbett, nr Kidderminster (01562) 777876
Edwardian hotel set in immature parkland. For a hotel
frequented almost exclusively by colleagues, it is friendly and
by no means stiff. The cooking is inconsistent and the chef's
eagerness to combine meat and fish needs to be held in check.

L SUN TO FRI, D EVERY DAY £90 DINNER, £45 LUNCH

BROWN'S 4
24 Quay St, Worcester (01905) 26263
A warehouse conversion beside the Severn. One wall is hung with
the sort of prints you don't want to take home. The cooking
remains firmly in the Western counties idiom established at The
Hole in the Wall thirty or forty years ago. Duck confit has not been
salted for long enough; a tomato tarte fin suffered from flavourless
fruit and from an over-intrusive red pepper paste; a crab cake was
on the bland side. The cheeses are splendid.

L TUES TO FRI AND SUN, D TUES TO SAT £100, SET LUNCH £58

CROQUE-EN-BOUCHE 5
221 Wells Rd, Malvern Wells (01684) 565612
The kitchen is capable of excellence, but not of consistency.
Dinners always begin with a tureen of soup. Thereafter skate with
coriander and mango, which is better than it sounds; croustade of
duck confit and apples; chicken with soup en pistou; smoked beef,
etc. Puddings are not a strong point. The selection of wines is
among the finest in the country and the prices are staggeringly low.

D THURS TO SAT £90+

GRAFTON MANOR 2
Grafton Lane, Bromsgrove (01527) 579007
A fine building, in part: Netherlandish crow-step gables,
diapered brickwork, an early classical porch, an originally
medieval chapel. The atmosphere is stiff and the interior
lugubrious. The place has seen better days. Dining room walls
are covered in flock. The carpet is tatty, the service chaotic.
Still, the cooking is just about all right. A jellied monkfish
terrine was a triumph of technique over flavour – it was almost
entirely insipid; duck confit was subjected to portion control
and was on the bland side. A chocolate tart was nice enough.

L AND D EVERY DAY £100

THE MILL AT HARVINGTON

1

Anchor La, Harvington, Evesham (01386) 870688
Beside the Avon among orchards and itinerant pickers' cara-
vans. The dining room is forever Thatcher's England – grey
and pink and chintzy; the cooking is old hat. Out-of-season
asparagus is one thing; out-of-season asparagus in the home
of English asparagus is another. Presentation is twee, flavours
are slight. The service is impeccable, though, and wines are
good – do not be put off by the ghastly vine-spiel.

L AND D EVERY DAY £65+

OLIVERS BRASSERIE

7

Broadway (01386) 854418
A sometime pub owned by the neighbouring Lygon Arms,
named after the Lord Protector and hung with portraits and
prints of that wild sybarite. The cooking is unquestionably
superior to any other I've had in Worcestershire. The prices
are low, the quality is high, the menu is hearteningly bereft of
fascinating ideas. Puréed potato is as good as anything Marco
or Nico can offer. Rilettes were served from ice cream scoops
with a world-class chutney; battered cod was done with rare
precision and was greaseless

L MON TO SAT, D EVERY DAY, BRUNCH ON SUN £60

PESCATORE

2

34 Sidbury, Worcester (0190) 521444
On the corner of a delicious 18th-century street, and entered
by a lavish portal which looks stuck on. The interior is older
than the exterior. It's all beams and bricks hung with bugles and
hunks of metal. Fontina and Tallegio are melted over roast veg,
quite successfully; tortellini were leathery; duck breast was
tough, overcooked, and served with indifferent sauté potatoes.

L AND D TUES TO SAT £50

SAFFRON

3

15 New St, Worcester (01905) 610505
A knockabout kind of place – the walls are colourfully dragged,
the furniture is stripped pine, the music is too loud, the service
too chummy. Duck magret was perfectly chargrilled; saffron
potatoes turned out to be chunks of parboiled potato dipped in
a chickpea flour batter flavoured with saffron then deep-fried;
provolone was cooked in parma ham and was pretty good.

L AND D EVERY DAY £45

East Anglia

Bedfordshire

Paris House   5
Woburn Park, Woburn (01525) 290692
Pretty good but sometimes overelaborate cooking by Roux
brothers' protégé Peter Chandler, whose superlative sweets
tend to be better than his forays into bourgeois dishes. Housed
in a mock-Tudor folly in a deer park; antlers everywhere.

L TUES TO SUN, D TUES TO SAT £130

Cambridgeshire

the Anchor Inn   3
Sutton Gault, Sutton, near Ely (01353) 778537
Hydrophobes beware. This handsome pantiled pub is beneath
the level of the New Bedford river beside it. The interior is
austerely elegant. Fish dishes are better than meat ones;
mackerel with orange and ginger sauce; a plate of mixed heftily
smoked specimens which includes green-lipped mussels, trout,
cockles, oysters; crab with herby mayo. Venison is overdone but
well sauced with juniper; beef is less competently prepared. The
choice of cheeses is enterprising but they are on the icy side.

L AND D EVERY DAY £60

the Old Bridge Hotel   2
1 High St, Huntingdon (01480) 424300
Anyone seeking a riverside seat is out of luck, for the dining
room is on the wrong side of the hotel. The cooking veers
alarmingly from near excellence to absolute bathos. In the
latter category comes a disgusting scallop and pork sausage
which is like a condom filled with dog food. But there is also
mushroom consommé with chicken-filled ravioli, guinea fowl
with a delicious gravy, a 'salad' of sweetbreads and langoustines. Good wines at fair prices. Decent service.

L AND D EVERY DAY £70+

the Old Fire Engine House   2
25 St Mary's St, Ely, Cambridgeshire (01353) 662582
English cooking which promises more than it delivers. This
handsome greyish brick restaurant a couple of hundred yards
from the west front of the cathedral goes to some trouble to
obtain local produce, such as pike and zander. But its cooking
does not match its shopping. Pike is overcooked and muddy
tasting. Best bets are casseroles, such as beef with Guiness
or rabbit. It's a pleasant and rather old-fashioned place.

L EVERY DAY, D MON TO SAT £60

THE THREE HORSESHOES
Madingley, Cambridge (01954) 210221

1

Antagonistic staff are forced to work an antagonistic queuing system. The kitchen is in thrall to sugar. Prices are daft. Good beer, though.

L AND D EVERY DAY £55

ESSEX

BAUMMANS BRASSERIE
4 Stoneham St, Coggeshall (01376) 561453

3

Once owned by Peter Langan, whose tenure is still evident in the menu. Best bets are straightforward lumps of duck or lamb with well-made sauces. Salads come off a production line; garlic bread is literally half-baked, pineapple sponge pudding is leaden.

L AND D WED TO SUN £65+

PARIS
719 London Rd, Westcliff-on-Sea (01702) 344077

1

Opposite a car lot and next to a crimper in an interminable suburban road. It has imported tone by the container load: vases with bent twigs, delicate paintings of mushrooms, peach and polar-blue art-deco mirrors... The men's toilet is decorated with coy photographic studies of nudes whose apparent purpose is to promote post-prandial satisfaction. The food is perhaps most notable for its consistent ability to remove flavour from dishes which are served with equally extraordinary slowness.

L THURS, FRI AND SUN, D TUES TO SAT £60

THE PIER AT HARWICH
The Quay, Harwich (0255) 241212

2

Great view of the Stour and Orwell estuary, pleasant service, nice enough cooking which is at its best when not attempting to be flashy. The fish and shellfish are notably fresh.

L AND D EVERY DAY £60+

THE STARR
Market Place, Great Dunmow (01371) 874321

2

This is not the Essex of scallies, car dealers and the friends of Venables; it is the Essex of brain-dead Sloanes and their braying mates, who fancy themselves as the bogusly tweedy Dudley Sutton character in *Lovejoy*. The bar here is cosy, dark green; the dining room is cool Pepsodent green. Cooking is mostly inept – sweetbreads are not cooked after blanching; risotto and oxtail are both flavourless; a sort of cassoulet is overcome by celery.

L EVERY DAY, D MON TO SAT £90

HERTFORDSHIRE

MIM'S 4
63 East Barnet Rd, New Barnet (020) 8449 2974
The setting in a drab suburb is anything but promising, but
the ambitious and unusual menu of French dishes raises
hopes. The execution, which is unmitigatingly rich, dashes
them. Brains are done in a bizarre gratin with cheese and
tomato; guinea fowl is stuffed with an eggy mousse.

L AND D TUES TO SUN £50

NORFOLK

ADLARDS 6
79 Upper St Giles St, Norwich (01603) 633522
A pretty restaurant in one of Norwich's many pretty streets.
The interior is alarmingly green and hung with some good little
paintings. The cooking is unlikely to astound with its fireworks,
but is diligent, considered and pleasing, even if flavours tend
to be slightly muted. Pastrywork is first-rate, the cheeses are
good, and the wines are nearly all good ones. If the British
quality of polite reserve is one you admire, then this is for you.

L TUES TO SAT, D MON TO SAT; £55 L, £90 D

THE HOSTE ARMS 5
The Green, Burnham Market (01328) 738777
Bar, restaurant, hotel and unofficial club in a village that is a
sort of Fulham-on-Sea. Owner Paul Whittome seems to want
to do for this place what Rick Stein has done for Padstow.
When the chef remembers that he's by the North Sea rather
than, say, the Strait of Malacca, he is pretty good – bass with
risotto, crab with cucumber 'noodles', cod with veal gravy, etc.
His orientalism is less engaging.

L AND D EVERY DAY £50

THE RAMBOUILLET 5
The Imperial Hotel, North Drive, Great Yarmouth
(01493) 842000
A rather grim Edwardian hotel further uglified by a tacky
plastic fascia of the early Seventies. Within, the basement is
all fin de siècle pastiche and non-stop Trenet and Piaf. The
cooking is simple and commendable: exemplary skate with
black butter and capers, cod and chips with tartare sauce,
top-quality kippers (and bloaters, when available). Good
draught beer, and a surprisingly posh wine list at reasonable
prices.

L SUN TO FRI, D EVERY DAY £60

ROCOCO AT THE CROWN
The Buttlands, Wells-next-the-Sea (01328) 710209

6

Neat, bright, individualistic place with cooking to match in an area that has little to offer. Recommended: herby salad with fried tongue; bass with a butter sauce and a tomato jam; duck confit with red wine and honey on fondant noodles; gratin dauphinois. Interesting wine list includes dessert wines from the Thames Valley.

D EVERY DAY £80

SUFFOLK

BUTLEY-ORFORD OYSTERAGE
Market Hill, Orford, Woodbridge (01394) 450277

2

A local institution that is smokery, shop and cafe all in one. The cafe is furnished with metal and wood chairs and the tables are spread with paper depicting mermen, trawlers, crab baskets, etc. The oysters are vast, plump and even more overtly sexy than usual. Smoked salmon is far from the shiny grot that increasingly goes under that name. It is recognisably salmon, though rather tarred. Eel is lighter; so, oddly, is cod roe. Coffee is horrible and possibly instant.

L AND D EVERY DAY £30

THE CROWN,
90 High St, Southwold (01502) 722275

2

Handsome and stylishly done-out hotel brimming with the ferociously genteel middle-class. It's owned by Adnam's, so the beer and wines are first-rate. The kitchen lags a long way behind. Dishes are badly mistimed and the reliance on cream sauces suggests a lack of ideas.

L AND D EVERY DAY £70+

THE LIGHTHOUSE
77 High St, Aldeburgh, (01728) 453377

8

Aldeburgh remains safely geriatric, a trad Dystopia-super-mare. Sara Fox and Guy Welsh are proper craftspeople; their standard of cooking scorns the dismal relativism which pleads for aberrations such as Sydney/Thai cooking. The Lighthouse possesses a sense of place; cooks what is locally available. Grilled lobster and kippered salmon were delicious, as was the steak. The walnut tart and toffee ice cream were ace.

L AND D EVERY DAY £50

THE STAR INN   5
Lidgate, Newmarket (01638) 500275

Pub pub rather than restaurant pub, but superior to many restaurant pubs. The owner is Catalan and it shows in her cooking and
in the place's quirks – bull's horn hoopla, Raimat, a dodgy print of
Dali's favourite (non Dali) painting. The finest dish is one of raw
salmon and scampi with olive oil and garlic. Lamb is overcooked,
in the Castillian manner, but still tastes good; steak is sauced with
stilton instead of, say, cabrales; queen scallops are cooked with
bacon in a sorrel broth; paella is pretty fair.

L EVERY DAY, D MON TO SAT £55

THE WHITE HART INN   8
11 High St, Nayland (01206) 263382

A lovely building that does excellent food that is aptly unpretentious
and douce. A world-class pork terrine is both dense and light, and
porkier, more savoury than expected. Duck confit is crisply skinned
and its meat is soft rather than fibrous. Lamb shoulder, slow-roasted
off the bone and daubed with an incredibly potent persillade which
combines ruggedness with precision. Saute potatoes are delicious,
as are the buttery veg. Lemon tart is glazed with torched sugar,
beautifully set and flavoured.

L AND D TUE TO SUN £60

NORTH EAST

CLEVELAND

ALSYROS

4

9 Upper Church St Hartlepool (01429) 272525

The food is straightforward, savoury, copiously portioned: a well-made duck liver pâté; bass with clams; duck breast with a fine fricassee of mushrooms, chorizo and pancetta. With this, a '95 Hochar, the second wine of the Bekkaa Valley's Ch Musar –not, it has to be said, what one expects to find in a hastily converted shop in the far North East. And all the more welcome for that.

L AND D MON TO SAT £50

TYNE & WEAR

CAFÉ 21

8

19-21 Queen St, Newcastle upon Tyne (0191) 222 0755

Terence Laybourne has transformed his first site: what was a full dress (though far from pompous) restaurant has expanded into the neighbouring premises and has, at the same time, gone open-necked. There has been no diminution of quality in the cooking. Spanish black pudding, morcilla, is served with big white beans braised with carrots; cod from South Shields is first-rate; Good cheeses, scrupulously chosen wines.

L AND D MON TO SAT £80

YORKSHIRE

THE BOX TREE

7

35–37 Church St, Ilkley, West Yorkshire (01943) 608484

The exterior is getting on for two hundred years old; the interior is a container-load of antiques – or junk. The food is often exquisite. The cooking is subtle, cute, odd: warm oysters with a light meat jus and broad beans; roast guinea fowl leg with the bird's leg steamed and an understated accompaniment of pancakes, butter sauce, cabbage.

L TUES TO SUN, D TUES TO SAT £86

BRASSERIE 44
44 The Calls, Leeds (0113) 234 3232

2

This is the groovy bit of Leeds, in a cluster of 'media' offices, wine bars, a pleasant hotel and two other restaurants. The bar is tacky: you sit on swings and listen to a player-piano with a blackamoor seated at it. Wheelchair access is claimed. But the ramp ends in steps, encouraging the wheeled to go for it. The cooking displays the same good intentions, the same approximate finish. That dated boondocks favourite, salmon pâté with smoked salmon, is lifted by a decent salsa verde.

L MON TO FRI, D MON TO SAT £60

THE GOLDEN LION
Village Square, Osmotherley, Northallerton, North Yorkshire (01609) 883526

8

The style and content are deliciously predictable. Execution is ace. Raw vegetables and a bagna cauda that bubbled over a spirit burner was as fine a version of this sauce as I've eaten. Also: beautifully battered strips of calamari with a properly made tartare sauce; chicken Kiev; casserole of lamb shoulder and lamb kidneys. There are a number of real ales: the laurels go to Nick Stafford's.

L AND D EVERY DAY £50+

McCoys, THE CLEVELAND TONTINE INN
Staddlebridge (junction of A19 and A172), Northallerton, North Yorkshire (01609) 882671

8

The singularity of this place is startling. It is as though the McCoy family has reinvented hotel-keeping and restauration. This is a family that cares about what it does, about how it treats its customers. It is all-embracingly generous. Marcus Bennett, the current chef, serves unpretentious dishes that are based on terrific ingredients. The flavours are big and vibrant, never coarse.

L AND D EVERY DAY £55+

MALLYAN SPOUT
Goathland, near Whitby, North Yorkshire (01947) 896206

5

A hotel on the moors near the early warning station at Fylingdales. There is a full-dress restaurant that opens in the evenings. At lunchtime you eat in the bar, and the menu is pub food – but what pub food! There is gravlax of the highest quality, there are succulent kippers from Whitby. Dog Tree Bank goat cheese is made nearby and is worth trying. Excellent clarets at bargain prices.

L IN THE BAR EVERY DAY £22

MELTON'S

6

7 Scarcroft Rd, York North Yorkshire (01904) 634341

A converted shop in York's drab southern suburbs. It's a sedate place livened by a brash art nouveau-ish mural. Hot salt cod is delicate, well-timed, correctly desalinated; it came with two sauces: aioli, which was unexceptionable, and a rather sharp, overelaborated tomato job which simply got in the way. Duck confit comes with a nicely dressed bunch of salad leaves, warm potatoes, diced cornichons and lightly pickled or marinated red onions.

L TUES TO SUN, D MON TO SAT £60+

THE PLOUGH INN

7

Saxton, Tadcaster, North Yorkshire (01937) 557242

Still a pub, just – but the cooking and the prices are those of a restaurant. The kitchen is skilful, confident, resourceful. Its own cured ham, served with celeriac aioli, is first-rate. Also recommended: ravioli filled with smoked salmon and langoustine. Well-chosen, moderately priced wines.

L TUES TO SUN, D TUES TO SAT £65+

North West

Cheshire

THE ALDERLEY EDGE HOTEL,
Macclesfield Rd, Alderley Edge (01625) 583033

4

Ostentatiously opulent version of a Victorian villa. The interior
is of the Bet Lynch school, and so are some of the punters.
The cooking is good when it slavishly imitates dishes from the
Roux brothers' repertoire; gutsy veal offal with garlic and
shallots, three meats with three sauces. The rest is no more
than ordinary and the cheeses are ghastly. The wine list is
wonderfully mad – 220 champagnes open it. The prices are
not especially kind.

L AND D EVERY DAY £75

THE ARKLE
Grosvenor Hotel, Eastgate Street, Chester (01244) 324024

6

Like the rest of central Chester, the hotel is an exemplar of
Victorian medievalism at its fruitiest. This ludicrously overpriced restaurant is a farrago of trompe l'oeil rustication,
gormless horsey paintings, pillars and swags. The cooking is
sometimes excellent – a pike mousse with oysters or a
preprandial 'snack' of oyster soup – but more often elaborately
workaday, striving to please Michelin (it worked) and to exhibit
the chef's prowess, which is considerable but not invariably
well-guided.

L TUES TO SUN, D TUES TO SAT £150

BELLE EPOQUE
60 King St, Knutsford (01565) 633060

2

The forest-green dining rooms are busily decorated in a
manner appropriate to the building's age (Art Nouveau
metalwork, fired tiles). The cooking is simple, but it should
be more consistent. A rump steak was unexceptional and
the chips were good. Cauliflower and cheese soup was well
executed; but battered fish was flavourless.

L TUES TO FRI AND SUN, D MON TO SAT £60

THE BRASSERIE
The Chester Grosvenor Hotel, Eastgate St, Chester
(01244) 324024

2

A convincing reproduction of a turn-of-the-century French
brasserie: leather banquettes, faience tiles, a stained-glass
lantern. The cooking is all right, but the tendency to mess
around with classic brasserie dishes is daft.

L AND D EVERY DAY £60

Nunsmere Hall 2
Tarporley Rd, Oakmere, Nr Chester (01606) 889100
A late-Victorian house among lakes in the Surrey of the North.
The service is incredibly slow, the cooking is buried beneath all
sorts of frills and tangential conceits. It could be quite good.
Puddings are good. The problem is that what precedes them is
also patissier's cooking. 'Hen's egg' with a mushroom fritter is
like some posh version of a motorway cafe breakfast. Sauces
tend to get shoved onto the wrong plate.

L AND D EVERY DAY £100+

Cumbria

Porthole 1
3 Ash St, Bowness on Windermere, Cumbria
(01539) 442793
Marine-themed, cramped, not much good. The cooking is
supposedly Italian, but lasagne is of about the standard you
might get in a student bedsit. The best thing is char, i.e., sea
trout from the lake. The wine list is extraordinary and impressive, quite out of kilter with the surroundings and the grub.

L WED TO FRI, SUN AND MON, D SUN TO MON £60

The Punchbowl 8
Crosthwaite, Cumbria (01539) 568237
Bargain price cooking. Rillettes and pork terrine are the work
of a consummate charcutier. Uncured salmon is cooked at
great heat and deliciously sauced with tomato, anchovy, mint
and capers. The local fruit is the damson, used to good effect
with duck. It's a pub and doesn't pretend to be anything else.

L TUES TO SUN, D TUES TO SAT £42

Lancashire

Paul Heathcote's 5
104 Higher Rd, Longridge (01772) 784969
Heathcote is a big name in northern restauration. He runs swish
modern brasseries in Preston and Manchester. This is his original
outfit – a whitewashed cottage on the outskirts of an industrial
village between the M6 and the Forest of Bowland. The interior is
cosy going on gemütlich. It is also littered with photographs of Mr
Heathcote, who makes a big thing of his locally inspired dishes.
But, this being a full-dress posh restaurant, there is a tendency to
over-refinement and to under-flavouring. Dishes sound better than
they taste. Still, Goosnargh duck is first-rate (though not helped by
undercooked potato), and roast beef is delicious.

L WED TO FRI AND SUN, D WED TO SUN £85+

SIMPLY HEATHCOTE'S   4
23 Winckley Sq, Preston (01772) 252732

Paul Heathcote's second, and more casual, restaurant. It looks good and the staff are civility itself. The cooking tends toward overelaboration. Still, the good-quality ingredients generally show through. Steak and chips is fine, so is pork with cider, calvados and an apple stuffed with cheese. Duck is not improved by dull peas and a rather unrefined sauce. Garbure is a balls-up.

L AND D EVERY DAY £60+

MANCHESTER

YANG SING   10
34 Princess St, Manchester (0161) 236 2200

The most appealing Cantonese cooking in Britain, in a most appealing restaurant. The place has a real buzz. It is very large, very crowded, very noisy. Like most other good Cantonese places it is chef-owned. Harry Yeung is evidently apprised of cuisines other than his native one. His meatballs are like quen-nelles, his spring rolls like Gascon croustades. Much of the excellent food is characterised by austere simplicity: veal chops seasoned with nothing but salt, straightforward roast pigeon, chicken wings steeped in garlic. Shellfish is very fine indeed.

L AND D EVERY DAY £50

SCOTLAND & WALES

SCOTLAND

EDINBURGH

ATRIUM
3

10 Cambridge St, Edinburgh (0131) 228 8882
Tortuously wrought chandeliers, tables made from railway
sleepers, off-vertical walls, webs of copper pipes with low
voltage bulbs at their end. The kitchen has some odd ideas
– cooking salami is one of them, serving al dente cabbage is
another.

L MON TO FRI, D MON TO SAT £75

DANIEL'S
2

88 Commercial St, Leith, Edinburgh (0131) 553 5933
The drearily bumptious menu is long and offers a bewildering
mix of mostly French dishes – cooked cheese items from the
Alps, confits from Gascony, some Alsacien standbys and,
naturally, pizzas. To judge by a choucroûte garni and a tarte
flambé, the kitchen aims for the coarse end of the market.

L AND D EVERY DAY £50

INDIAN CAVALRY CLUB

2

3 Atholl Place, Edinburgh (0131) 228 3282/2974

An oddity – a sub-continental restaurant with an entirely
bourgeois clientele who wouldn't know a pool of stewed phal
if they trod in it. Apart from framed prints of durbars, the
decor is occidental. The staff wear a uniform which suggests
both bellboys and Kwik-Fit operatives; the food is a bit up and
down. Peripheral items, such as pineapple samber (sic), tarka
dhal and rice with chick peas, are to be preferred to virtually
identical lamb and chicken curries. Drink lassi.

L AND D EVERY DAY £45

MALMAISON BRASSERIE

1

1 Tower Place, Leith, Edinburgh (0131) 468 5000

The trouble with the Malmaison chain of hotels is that the
things they do well are, ultimately, the unimportant ones:
buildings, decor, the staff's clothes. A plateful of pretty good
mussels, a miserly portion of smoked salmon with nice blinis,
a couple of acceptable steaks, cabbage braised with bacon was
sensibly unambitious cooking and generally competently done,
but it was marred by the accompaniment of loud pop music.

L AND D EVERY DAY £50

RESTAURANT MARTIN WISHART

4

54 The Shore, Leith, Edinburgh (0131) 553 3557

What Wishart does, he does competently, but the very genre
he espouses is flawed. It is the all-too-familiar story of dishes
undone by their multiplicity of ingredients and the flower-arranger
tendency to the fore. One dish included turbot, foie gras and
salmon mousse, morels, potato, spinach, some sort of frothed-up
sauce. Generally, more means worse, and that is the case here.

L AND D TUES TO SAT £80+

SHORE

0

3 The Shore, Leith, Edinburgh (0131) 553 5080

The dining room is off the loud bar of a smoky boozer. The
cooking is disgraceful. Squid was dished up on top of
undressed salad leaves and lumps of raw pepper; mackerel
was far from fresh; langoustines were overcooked. Avoid.

L AND D EVERY DAY £45+

VALVONA AND CROLLA   5
19 Elm Row, Edinburgh (0131) 556 6066

One of the finest salumeria and enoteca in Britain has now established its own restaurant in a long, narrowish addition to its premises. The cooking is simple and delightful. Tomato soup is sweet, full, smooth, creamy. Rocket salad is massively enhanced by parmesan of singular quality. The service is charming and efficient.

B AND L MON TO SAT £50

THE VINTNERS ROOMS,   6
The Vaults, 87 Giles St, Leith, Edinburgh (0131) 554 6767

The dining room in this 300-year-old warehouse is high and handsome and candle-lit by fine chandeliers. The kitchen is among Edinburgh's best. Wild boar boudin, a very high-class sausage, is done with a puree of apple and sweet wine; guinea fowl is overshadowed by a faggot-like forcemeat ball.

L AND D MON TO SAT £85

FIFE

THE PEAT INN   6
Cupar, Fife (01334) 840206

This restaurant belongs to a genus that's common in France: the formerly humble out-of-the-way tavern that has been spruced to within an inch of its essence. The cooking, though, is skilful, unshowy. 'Cassoulet' is really a pot au feu of pork, lamb, duck and Toulouse sausage in a beautifully rich duck stock; large and par-ticularly fresh scallops are grilled and served with a pea puree.

L AND D TUES TO SAT £90+

GLASGOW

ROGANO   2
11 Exchange Place, Glasgow (0141) 248 4055

The Thirties exterior and the jazz-modern interior are worth the detour, but you can't eat them. What you can eat is middle-of-the-road cooking at inflated prices. The fish is a bit better than the meat – it used to be an exclusively fish restaurant. White wines are consequently superior to reds.

L AND D EVERY DAY £100

STRAVAIGIN
8 Ruthven Lane, Glasgow (0141) 334 7165

5

The name is misleading: no one could possibly stray into these tiny hidden premises. Two young women, one with a New York/Glasgow accent, run the place with good cheer, and the kitchen knows what it's doing – which is keeping it simple. Mussels are of superlative quality and their treatment with a garlic and basil broth was splendid; salmon fish cakes taste of that fish; a blue steak of first-rate rib eye is served with nothing but a well-judged seasoning. A short selection of wines is sold at generous prices and there are a number of decent beers in formidably outsized bottles.

L AND D EVERY DAY £45

HIGHLAND REGION

CLIFTON HOTEL
Viewfield St, Nairn, Highlands (01667) 453119

3

Individualistic hotel overlooking the Moray Firth. The dining room is done out with morbid exuberance. Some of the cooking is good – a Spanish dish of pig's kidneys, meatballs, tomato sauce and pimenton, for instance. The Scottish cheeses are notable and the wine list is splendid.

L AND D EVERY DAY £70

INVERLOCHY CASTLE
Torlundy, Fort William, Highland Region (01397) 702177

4

An extraordinary Victorian time capsule, which tries to be more country house than hotel. The service is quite something – a uniformed platoon greet diners who, inevitably, have difficulty negotiating the massed ranks. The interior of the muscular baronial pile is impressive hectares of panelling, hundreds of dead stags' heads, overwrought furniture by Louis the Decorator and Louis the Highlander. The setting beneath Ben Nevis is also more than startling. Cooking is regulation issue luxury hotel stuff, all pretty well-cooked, but lacking any individual stamp; the meat however, especially the beef, is first-rate.

L AND D EVERY DAY £100

INVERNESS

DUNAIN PARK

2

On the A82, two miles south of Inverness, Scotland
(01463) 230512

The place is homely, the cooking is not – it attempts more than it can deliver and seems reluctant to keep things simple. When the sound ingredients are not mucked around, the results are pleasing. Excellent wines, good views.

D EVERY DAY, BOOKINGS NEEDED £70

MORAY

OLD MONASTERY

2

The Drybridge, Buckie Moray (01542) 832660

More a rebuilding than a conversion, this spacious and handsome establishment looks down across Pict land to the Moray Firth. The cooking tends toward provincial elaboration, but is on target with the simpler dishes. The wine list is good.

L AND D TUES TO SAT £80

WEST LOTHIAN

CHAMPANY INN

3

Champany, Linlithgow, Scotland (0150) 6834532

The ne plus ultra of the steak house. A very strange outfit indeed. The meat is 'grown' by the owners but is, sometimes, carelessly cooked. The gravlax is the best in Lothian. Service is churchy, pretentious. A genuine oddity and one that is worth risking if you can afford £100.

L MON TO FRI, D MON TO SAT £100

WALES

LE CASSOULET

6

5 Romilly Crescent, Canton, Cardiff (02920) 221905

You know where you are with a restaurant called Le Cassoulet:
you're in a Toulouse of the stomach, a Toulouse of the spirit. This
is an enjoyable and very correct outfit: it eschews gimmickry, it
makes a substantial effort to please. The cassoulet is respectable,
properly put together and cooked slowly. Steamed foie gras was
excellent, so was a dish of chicken with chicken risotto and
chicken jus. The service is charming, the prices are fair.

L AND D TUES TO SAT; L £40, D £80

GANNETS BISTRO

0

7 St James's Square, Aberystwyth, Ceredigion
(01970) 617164

Astonishingly bad; mines strata of ghastliness that defy
comparison. The food is school food of thirty years ago. At its
best it is straight off the supermarket shelf – smoked mackerel
is warmed up like kippers; duck pâté is dismal. Grotesquely
overcooked grey lamb is served with gunk and mint. Pork –
even fouler than the lamb – is served with the same gunk, a
sort of wallpaper paste posing as 'gravy', and with packet
stuffing. Carrot puree is all water. The staff come from the
boarding-house janitocracy.

L AND D WED TO SAT AND MON £30

THE WALNUT TREE INN

9

Llandewi Skirrid, Abergavenny, Gwent (01873) 852797

It took Franco and Ann Taruschio thirty years not to change
this beautifully sited pub into a restaurant. It is crowded,
matey, beguiling. The point of the place is gustatory pleasure.
A peerless vincigrassi stands alongside salted duck. The bre-
saola is fabulously fondant. Wales' greatest restaurant was
taken over in 2001 by Francesco Mattioli and Steven Terry,
who surely know better than to change it.

L AND D TUES TO SUN £85

OVERSEAS

Argentina

Buenos Aires

9 Del Julio

3

**C. Pellegrini 587, Capital Federal, Buenos
Aires** (00) 541143222501
Up-market parrilla. The conservative repertoire is not as
precisely prepared as it should be for these prices. Grilled
offal is too charred; meat from the asado is dry; provolone
is insufficiently cooked.

L AND D EVERY DAY £35

Los Anos Locos

3

**Avenida Rafael Obligado y La Pampa, Costanero
Norte, Capital Federal, Buenos Aires** (00) 54114784861
On the coast near Aeroparque Jorge Newbery is a group of
roadhouses which cry out for Robert Mitchum and Jane Greer.
This one doubles up as a parrilla, is variously barrel-vaulted,
whitewashed, pebbledashed and brashly tiled. Standard issue
grilled offal and steak.

L AND D EVERY DAY £30

CLARIDGE HOTEL

Tucuman 535, Capital Federal, Buenos Aires
(00) 541143147700

There are three reasons for patronising this relic of the 1940s.
First, the bar, which is akin to that of a Surrey golf club but
has an incomparable septuagenarian barman called Eugenio,
who mixes proper cocktails. Second, to get your luggage stolen
from the lobby and watch the bored reaction of the offhand,
negligent staff. Third, to eat a sort of ersatz haute cuisine
which suggests that Fanny and John Craddock have been
exhumed to run the kitchen. Eggs Po Pobarsky is poached eggs
(not quite cooked) in a fried-bread box the size of a halfbrick
covered with glutinous sauce which recalls at best chicken à la
king and at the worst, something out of a Vesta packet.

L AND D MON TO FRI £35

DORA

**Leandro N. Alen 1016, Capital Federal,
Buenos Aires** (00) 541143112891

Soberly bourgeois establishment which retains its 1940s decor:
pale wood and cream walls, white napery. The cooking is
considered, comforting and generously portioned even by the
standards of a city which specialises in copiousness. Elvers are
done in the Basque manner with garlic and oil; steak is, most
unusually, garnished – with peas stewed with ham, skinned
peppers and potatoes like thick crisps; shredded spinach is
fried with garlic. Importunate service.

L AND D MON TO SAT £35

EL CRIOLITO

**Avenida Tres Fronteras, Puerto Iguazu, Provincia
de Misiones, Buenos Aires** (no telephone)

Within a few hundred metres of both Paraguay and Brazil and
thus ultra-Argentinian, this small border town is downstream
from the South American Niagara, Iguazu Falls. This is a
charming restaurant which does a great empanadilla filled with
chard and hard-boiled egg and first-rate steak and chips with
a tremendous salsa made from garlic, parsley, oregano, chilli,
white wine vinegar and olive oil.

£24

EL PALACIO DE LA PAPA FRITA

Lavalle 735, Capital Federal, Buenos Aires
(00) 541143935849

The smartest in a short chain of brasserie-like operations
which specialise in the most delicious souffle'd potatoes.
The steaks are first class too. The combination of quality
and amazingly low prices mean it's always full.

L AND D EVERY DAY £10

EL TRAPICHE

5

Paraguay 5099, Capital Federal, Buenos Aires
(00) 541147727343

Labyrinthine canteen with raw brick walls, industrial girders, brash tiles and a real buzz. Cured hams hang from the high ceiling. Their unusually piquant meat is good. This is also a notable address for paella, made with basmati rice; it also includes chicken, octopus, prawns, asparagus and tinned palm hearts.

L AND D EVERY £10

KATRINE

2

Avenida Alicia M de Justo 138, Capital Federal, Buenos Aires (00) 541143156221

The former customs buildings and bonded warehouses of Puerto Madero have been Conran'd over the past few years. They house scores of restaurants and cafes. This one is all aspiration and little achievement. The owner/chef is Norwegian, and in the heart of Buenos Aires she attempts to do a sort of generalised Franco-Italian cooking notable for its misplaced accents. Spaghetti with ceps and garlic succeeds in lacking any discernible flavour; creamy cep sauce with tornedos is also underpowered.

L AND D MON TO FRI, D SAT £80

PAPER MOON

4

Estacion San Isidro, San Isidro, Provincia de Buenos Aires (no telephone)

In a shopping precinct attached to a refurbished station on the line up to the Tigre Delta. The architectually confused surroundings and underpatronised shops are rather dismal, but this is a surprisingly good restaurant. Stewed calamari are served with blanched lemons; green gnocchi or ravioli are stuffed with spinach and cheese and served with a white wine butter sauce.

£50

PIPPO

3

Parana 356, Capital Federal, Buenos Aires
(00) 541143746365

There is a vast concentration of popular eating houses on and around the neon canyon of Avenida Corrientes. To get the total lack of decoration which informs Pippo you'd pay through the nose in London. Here, it comes absurdly cheap, along with basic dishes of some distinction – morcilla, chorizo, breaded chicken escalope, chips, and a distinctively thick form of spaghetti.

L AND D MON TO SAT £10

BELGIUM

BRUSSELS

L'ACHEPOT
5

place St-Catherine 1, Brussels (00) 3225116221
A bit like a pub where there's always a sort of party going on.
The cooking is basic and good: shrimp croquettes actually
taste of shrimp; a lardon salad was so copiously dressed it was
more like soup; tiny boudins, black and white; andouillette
with sauté potatoes. The service is efficient and friendly.

L AND D MON TO SAT £15; NO CARDS

AUX ARMES DE BRUXELLES
7

rue des Bouchers 13, Brussels (00) 3225112118
This is a restaurant that is above all correct: white tablecloths,
white-coated waiters, limed art-deco oak, zinc surfaces. The
repertoire is that of a classic brasserie. Lobster with braised
chicory in a herby cream is beguiling; tomato with grey
shrimps was just that: perfect fruit, crustaceans and mayo.

L AND D TUES TO SUN £75+

IN'T SPINNEKOPKE
5

place du Jardin aux Fleurs 1, Brussels (00) 3225118695
A cosy place that makes the most of its age (it is of the late
18th-century, which is long lived for a vernacular, as opposed
to a grand, building in this city): nicotine-yellow ceiling,
flowery wallpaper, pewter jugs, wooden banquettes.
Waterzooi of salmon and sea wolf, a.k.a. catfish, is skilfully
made; fromage de tête is also pleasing; steak is flavourless,
presumably from insufficient hanging; tarte tatin is caramelised
to the point of tasting like toffee apple.

L MON TO FRI, D MON TO SAT £50

FRANCE

PARIS

L'AMBASSADE D'AUVERGNE
8

22 rue de Grenier, St-Lazare, Paris 3
(00) 33142723122
Small, ancient, beamed, tiled. The immemorial dishes of the
Massif Central are real heavyweights, and include the potato
and cantal cheese purée, aligot.

L AND D EVERY DAY £65

LES AMOGNES

8

243 rue du Faubourg-St-Antoine, Paris 11
(00) 33143727305
Chef Thierry Coué has a light touch in potentially heavy
dishes, ingenuity, resourcefulness with 'humble' ingredients,
a subtle and original palate. Perfect beignets of near-liquid
salt cod brandade were very good; hachis parmentier was
delicious. The non-prizewinning anti-decor consists of bare
stone walls covered with photos of African children.

L TUES TO FRI, D MON TO SAT £50

AU BASCOU

8

38 rue Reaumur, Paris 3 (00) 33142726925
This place goes in for local colour: rustic beams, haphazard
plastering, tongue-and-groove dado, paintings of Basque fisher-
folk and a large black-and-white print of the beach at Biarritz.
The owner is a former sommelier, who used to work for the
great Alain Dutournier, and his list of modestly priced wines
from the further southwest is fascinating. 'Confit' tomato is
served with tuna rillettes; foie gras is fried with buttery apple
segments; braise of beef with unsalted anchovies plonked on
top is splendid.

L TUE TO FRI, D MON TO SAT £55

AU TROU GASCON

10

40 rue Taine, Paris 12 (00) 33143443426
For more than twenty years Alain Dutournier's pretty belle
epoque outfit – more a super-bistro than a grand restaurant –
has been the pick of Paris's southwestern establishments. The
hyper-real takes on a familiar repertoire include: oysters in the
bordelaise manner with piping hot 'sausages'; crisp, spatch-
cocked duck confit with a cep 'cake'; layered potato foie gras
with truffles; the cassoulet to beat all cassoulets – it is soupy,
savoury and light. Excellent and recondite wines, splendid
desserts. Affable, hieratic service.

L MON TO FRI, D MON TO SAT £90+

BENOIT

8

20 rue St-Martin, Paris 4 (00) 33142722576
Distinguished and ancient bistro which adheres to the practice
of displaying sample dishes before its customers. The service is
endlessly courteous.

L AND D EVERY DAY £65

BOFINGER 6
5 rue Bastille, Paris 4 (00) 33142728782
Classic brasserie in the art-nouveau style of Le Petit Palais:
brass, coloured glass, etc. A convivial joint, and the cooking's
pretty good, too.

L AND D EVERY DAY £65

CARRE DES FEUILLANTS 10
14 rue de Castiglione, Paris 1 (00) 33142868282
This is where the great Dutournier himself cooks. It is
undeniably swanky, undeniably expensive – but you are paying
for more than three hours' cosseting and gastronomic bliss,
you're paying for this chef's thirty years of zealous intelligence
applied to the cooking of his native Gers. No one does it
better. The balance of flavours is perfect. So, too is the balance
of the rustic and the classical. Recommended: elvers with
garlic, parsley and Bayonne ham; a 'pie' of layered dove and
foie gras with a jelly spiked with sweet/sour fruits; Chalosse
beef with bonemarrow and tarragon served with chips cooked
in goose fat; fruits poached in Earl Grey with brioche perdue.
Fabulous wines and a superb Fourme d'Ambert.

L MON TO FRI, D MON TO SAT £160+

CHARLOT ROI DES COQUILLAGES 5
12 place de Clichy, Paris 9 (00) 33153204800
The art deco interior has been lynched by a self-confident
disco designer: mirrored, marbled dining room with swirly
carpets and baroque chandeliers. The cooking, too, possesses
the self-confidence to keep itself simple. Oysters and crab
were followed by grilled lobster, grilled langoustines and a
grand aioli comprising unsalted cod, boiled eggs, boiled carrots
and turnips. The suited service is charmingly urbane and the
list includes Domaine Ott's rosé which perennially lives up to
its reputation.

£70+, SET L AND D £45.

CHEZ GEORGES 6
273 bd Pereire, Paris 17 (00) 33145743100
This is opposite the Palais de Congres, near the site of the old
Luna Parc at Porte Maillot. The cooking is diligently prepared,
unflashy, correct. An unusually light tête de veau is sauced
with an unusually well-gauged sauce gribiche – a standard dish
rendered with expertise. Well-flavoured gigot is carved at the
table with panache. The service is delightful. The petits vins
are a snip.

£75

CHEZ MICHEL
10 rue de Belzunce, Paris 10 (00) 33144530620

It doesn't get much better than this. Three hours from London
Waterloo on Eurostar, three minutes on foot from the Gare du
Nord. Thierry Breton's approach to restauration is back to
basics. The dining room is scruffy enough to make one wonder
whether this is wise: fake beams, chipped tiles. As soon as M
Breton's cooking is tasted all doubts evanesce. A great lunch
included warm oysters with tiny croûtons and rock salt;
mussels cooked in silver paper with thyme and bay; marvellous
roast goose with tiny boudins noirs and boudins blancs; perfect
salt cod brandade. The wines are nearly all petits vins under
£15. Service is charming.

L AND D TUES TO SAT £60

CHEZ PAUL
13 rue de Charonne, Paris 11 (00) 3314700 3457

The restaurant's interior bears testimony to its 75-year life:
nicotine brown walls and authentically cramped tables.
Service, however, is non-authentic. The women lack the
carelessness, negligence and insolence that Londoners
routinely suffer. Rabbit rillettes, bone marrow with cornichons
and toast, fois gras terrine with pear poached in spiced red
wine, beef tartare with capers, shallots and garlic – all seasoned and pampered with absolute precision – all thankfully
uninventive and far from cutting-edge.

£45, SET L AND D £30

CHEZ PHILIPPE
106 rue de la Folie Mericourt, Paris 11 (00) 33143573378

Old-fashioned, reliable, unflashy. The menu is part
Burgundian, part south-western, wholly traditional. Real
food at sensible prices.

L AND D MON TO FRI £65

LA COUPOLE,
102 bd Montparnasse, Paris 14 (00) 33143201420

One of the greatest Parisian brasseries, whose refurbishment
in the late Eighties was not to all tastes – the patina of the
years was stripped off. It is now a replica of its original self.
For such a vast outfit – it seats about 500 – the cooking is
surprisingly good, and much better than before the makeover.
Not that the cooking is why people come here. They come
because every night is an event. It's that simple.

OPEN UNTIL 2AM EVERY DAY £60

FOUR SEASONS GEORGE V
31 av George V, Paris 8 (00) 33149527000

10

The George V should really be called the Louis, after Louis
the decorator. Containerloads of tapestries, gilded console
tables, marble busts, rococo mirrors, and so on have been
brought from rué St Honore. The place is bursting with everything save self-restraint. It goes without saying that the restaurant does swell lines in pomp and neo-directoire pediments.
Two sorts of salt, two sorts of butter, absolutely no chance of
pouring your own wine. The cooking is sumptuous, magnificent, not least because it quite lacks the chi-chi that mars
much hotel cooking. A veal chop with macaroni was splendid;
a truffled game pie of forcemeat, hare and pheasant goes
straight into the all-time top ten. Wines: predictably big
names at predictably big prices.

L AND D EVERY DAY £160; SET LUNCH, £110

JULES VERNE
2nd Level, Eiffel Tower, Paris 7 (00) 33145556144

7

The immediate views of this vertical Forth Bridge are
captivating. And even were the restaurant situated at street
level, it would still be worth patronising. The cooking is
precise, considered, mostly balanced. Recommended: snail
soup with a mushroom raviolo; cromesquis of potato and
bone marrow; chicken breast with gravy and a Lancashire hot
pot of potato and chicken leg; skate with a duxelles stuffing;
bergamot ice cream. Haughtily offhand service.

L AND D EVERY DAY £150

LE MEURICE
228 rue de Rivoli, Paris 1 (00) 33144581010

8

The hotel is a Versailles for the bourgeoisie. The building is so
large, so labyrinthine, and there is just so much of everything –
marble, glass, mirror, gold – that cornucopia soon becomes the
norm. The dining room is staffed by several armies of tailed
waiters and equipped with no end of trolleys and incendiary
devices. The cooking excels when it tends toward the down-
home - rather incongruous in such a setting – but disappoints
when going in for conventional grand hotel stuff. Scallops with
sloppy risotto are very good, as is a pumpkin-based soup with
chunks of chestnut and caramelised gingerbread; roast pig and
roast goose are both good. There's one problem: the pianist.
Shoot?

L AND D EVERY DAY £110

LA REGALADE

10

49 av Jean-Moulin, Paris 14 (00) 33145456858

One of the hottest tickets in town. The formula is simple
enough: a truly brilliant chef, a fixed-price menu – £17 for
three courses – and 60 covers shoehorned into a former cafe
smaller than a squash court. Scallops of the utmost sweetness
are grilled in the shell; an entire beef marrow is removed from
the bone and roasted; hachis parmentier is routinely translated
as shepherd's pie, but I doubt that our native ewe-abusers ever
had one quite as good as this.

L TUES TO FRI AND SUN, D TUES TO SUN £55

LE VIOLON D'INGRES

5

135 rue St-Dominique, Paris 15 (00) 33145551505

Christian Constant's restaurant is like nothing so much as the
most pretentious address in some provincial town, Nevers, say.
There are the terrible primary-coloured oils that boondocks
France specialises in, there are the flower patterned
banquettes, the acres of tan veneer, the mirrors... The cooking
is technically virtuous, but is mostly on the insipid side of
bland, rich yet dull. The shining exceptions were a marvellous
version of livre à la royale and a tarte fin of truffles, bacon and
onion puree. Service was offhand and patronising.

L AND D EVERY DAY £100+

NORTH EAST

ALSACE LORRAINE

AU NID DE CIGOGNE

8

rue 18-Novembre, 67190 Mutzig (00) 33388381197

The building opposite the castelled brewery is joke oak of
c.1900. Inside it's pub-like with a huge, tiled stove, a massive
boar's head, standard-issue Alsatian chairs with a heart-shaped
aperture. The cooking is top-notch. Presskopf, a.k.a. fromage
de tête, a.k.a. brawn was made with great expertise; coq au
riesling was fantastically fully flavoured and came with spaetzle
of an almost soufflé'd consistency. To finish: young munster
with walnut oil.

L THURS TO TUES, D THURS TO MON £45

BUREHIESEL

9

4 parc Orangerie, 67000 Strasbourg (00) 3388616264
The premises are a farmhouse brought from a neighbouring
village and then re-erected for the Strasbourg Industrial
Exhibition of 1896. Antoine Westermann is a formidable chef
with an astonishing range. Among his creations are: roast eel
with a world-class potato salad; beer-flavoured brioche with
beer ice cream and a pear poached in beer.

L AND D FRI TO TUES £130

CHEZ YVONNE

8

10 rue de Sanglier, 67000 Strasbourg (00) 3388328415
Yvonne Haller is a local institution, and it's not difficult to
see why: the cooking is excellent, the service solicitous. Tête
de veau is perfectly cured meat dressed with a vinaigrette
composed of white wine vinegar, neutral oil, bouillon, sylvaner,
pink onions and chives. Ceps are braised in cream.

L TUES TO SAT, D MON TO SAT £70

MUNSTERSTEUWEL

6

8 place du Marche-aux-Cochons-d-lait, Strasbourg
(00) 3388321763
Pork trotter stuffed with sweetly cured jambonneau, pommes
boulangère, rather mousse-like onion tart on a merveloussly
crisp base, ceps with persillade, a pichet of light riesling,
a glass of baie de houe... The every-day cooking of Alsace is
a wonderful thing, and this amiable outfit near Strasbourg's
vertiginous cathedral is a good place to try it.

L AND D EVERY DAY

LE COLLET

5

On D417, 12km east of 88400 Gerardmer
(00) 33329600957
The dining room is all wood and knick-knacks slung from beams
and walls. It is the only restaurant I've seen which displays a
collection of blowtorches. The cooking is pretty straightforward,
though hardly farmyard: a pâté en croute with cornichons and a
powerful beetroot pickle; tête de veau with a thinned mayo and
artichoke; a gargantuan piece of beef with a sticky red wine
sauce and thick chips; roast apple with gingerbread ice cream.

L AND D THURS TO TUES £60

FERME-AUBERGE DE LIEZEY
On D50, 11km west of 88400 Gerardmer
(00) 33329630951

5

No chi-chi: agri-implements on the walls and checked cloths on the tables. The produce here is good, flavoursome, simply prepared. A vosgien version of tartiflette uses a mix of munster and a tomme called vachelin – these are melted onto a combination of potatoes and lardons. This is delicious. So was a pork potee of smoked ribs, smoked sausage and smoked loin. A light pinot noir is served in pichets. The service is charming, entirely hospitable; the bill absurdly low.

L AND D TUES TO SUN (CLOSED NOV–DEC) £30

HOSTELLERIE DES BAS RUPTS
on D486, 4km south of 88400, Gerardmer
(00) 33329630925

2

One to avoid – though you have to go quite a way, to southern Vosges, to avoid it. The cooking is better on finicky details than on the core of a dish. Two sorts of smoked trout, brown and rainbow, were all right. But tripe cooked with riesling, cream and mustard suffered from the use of what tasted like medium-sweet wine. Pork cutlets were tough and came with twee cylinders of mash and black pudding. Fresh munster is excellent.

L AND D EVERY DAY £85

BRITANNY

LA GODILE
port Mer, 35260 Cancale (00) 3399896565

5

Friendly restaurant which overlooks the bay of Mont St Michel. Its aspirations may be limited but it thoroughly achieves them. It serves massive quantities of raw shellfish (Cancale is an oyster town) and follows up with massive quantities of meat grilled over a log fire near the front door. Terrific chips.

L AND D EVERY DAY £40

RESTAURANT DE BRICOURT
1 rue Dugluescin 35260, Cancale (00) 3399896476

6

The major French guides Michelin, Gault Milau and Bottin Gourmand rate this higher than any other place for miles around. The early 19th-century house is certainly charming and elegant; the reception is polished; the service rather grand. And the cooking is admirable, which is the problem. One is more liable to marvel at the technical ingenuity of the chef than to actually enjoy his food. His cleverness is untempered by joy. However, as modern temples of gastronomy go, it is blessedly bereft of pomposity and not stupidly expensive.

L AND D THURS TO MON £80

LA ROTONDE
1 bd Chateaubriand, Paramé (00) 3399404797

3

An ancient hotel restaurant approached by way of a pool table
and a curved bar, whose clientele is spectacularly sordid, the
kind of people who end up in human interest stories in *Ici Paris*
and *France Soir*. Competent, if incredibly basic grub but a
thousand times better than you'd find on, say the Isle of Wight.
Oysters, steak, chips, simple soups are all unexceptional.

CLOSED SUNDAY NIGHT AND MONDAY, BUT OPEN ALL WEEK IN JULY
£15+

BRASSERIE DES VOYAGEURS
place Chateaubriand 35400, St-Malo (00) 3399564539

2

You can sit here and watch special export quality British yobs
do their stuff. When Our Finest aren't strutting their pathetic
stuff, this square is filled with purposeful Local Colour folk
songstresses and their pimps, Africans selling Senegalese
sunglasses as worn by Ray Charles. Eat andouillette or steak
with chips, and oysters.

L AND D EVERY DAY £25

LA ROSE DES SABLES
8 rue Amiral-Magon, St-Servan, (00) 3399823248

4

A delightful improbability. A building like a village hall converted
into a Marrakesh tent with carpets on the ceiling and brass trays
on the walls. Some of the Moroccan cooking is pretty much
the works: couscous with mutton; brochettes of mixed meats;
chickpea stew. The Algerian Coteaux de Mascara is undrinkable.

L WED TO SUN, D TUES TO SUN £35

Nord Pas de Calais

Les Marissons
pont de la Dodane, St-Leu, 80000 Amiens
(00) 33322929666
This former boathouse is entered through a little garden of such
prissy tweeness that one's heart sinks. Restaurants don't come
much more determinedly provincial than this small-town essay
in big-city sophistication. The staff have been instructed in formal gambits but are simply gauche. Knick-knacks are particularly
hideous. The cooking is pretentious. Flavourless meat dishes
came with six different (and uninteresting) vegetables.

L TUES TO FRI AND SUN, D TUES TO SAT £90+

L'Os a Moelle
12 rue Flatters, 80000 Amiens (00) 33322927546
The wholehearted espousal of the Brentford Nylons look doesn't
augur well; but the chef can cook. Several menus, actually, with
at least half a dozen confusing formulas. A thin baguette stuffed
with snails and garlic was a robust example of the higher fry-up
school. Hampe is the local name for onglet; it is served with
chips and noodles. Pot au feu includes the marrow bones the
restaurant is named for.

L AND D TUES TO SUN £40

La Faisanderie
45 Grand'Place, 62000 Arras (00) 33321482076
This restaurant occupies a barrel-vaulted cellar of brick and
limestone. Bollinger's pinot noir is not recommended: everything else is: cheese tart, marinated sardines, warm boudin of
smoked eel, hare and pork brochette with a compote of prunes
and orange peel, veal with a macaroni gratin and cep sauce, a
dessert of sweetened tomato and beetroot with truffle ice
cream, hot chocolate soufflé.

£140

Bar Hamiot
1 rue Faidherbe, 62200 Boulogne-sur-Mer
(00) 33321314420
The restaurant, part of a hotel in a postwar block, advertises
itself with a 20ft-tall neon waiter clasping a jug of foaming beer
and with the legend specialites boulonnaises, which apparently
include choucroûte and couscous. Steak hache actually tastes
of meat; the chips are all right. Fines de Claire and moules
marinieres were OK. Coffee is potent; the prices notably low.

L AND D EVERY DAY £35

LE PARIS PLAGE

5

31 rue St-Jean, 62520 Le Touquet (00) 33321055959
An unassuming and amiable brasserie which serves a fine
salmon carpaccio, an adequate steak hache, delicious
strawberry ice cream and an andouillette of stellar quality
from Cambrai.

L AND D EVERY DAY £30

A L'HUITRIERE

9

3 rue des Chats Bossus, 59800 Lille (00) 33320554341
The best cooking I've had in the north of France. The chef
turns northern cooking into high cooking without losing its
essence. Escalope of foie gras is poached, then roasted and
served with lightly braised cabbage; eel fillets are sauced with
beer vinegar and accompanied by whole garlic cloves and the
kind of herb salad that relies on absolute freshness.

L EVERY DAY, D MON TO SAT £120

AUBERGE FLEURIE

8

**67 rue General de Gaulle, 59216
Sars-Poteries** (00) 33327616248
A handsome roadside inn 50 miles southeast of Lille.
Pike-perch is a superb fish done with a sauce based on aged
genever. Salmon is served raw with fragrant oil; coq a la bier
is a revelation. The local cheeses are lovely.

L EVERY DAY, D MON TO SAT £100

LE HOCHEPOT

3

6 rue de Nouveau-Sicle, 59800 Lille (00) 33320541759
On the ground floor of a neglected Seventies development.
The lugubrious interior features a dark wood ceiling and
plants to occlude the light. There are, however, handsome
electroliers. House apero – genever with cassis and redcurrants
– is for the very curious. Goyère, which evidently has some
etymological connection with gougère, is a slightly different
confection, being a maroilles tart. It was good, coq à la bière
wasn't. The fowl was crudely jointed, bony, tough and coarsely
flavoured with an overdose of juniper berries. Alongside it was
a pile of sweet red cabbage and warm potato salad bound in
mayo. The cheeses are OK and the service is fairly jolly.

L MON TO FRI, D MON TO SAT £60+

LE SEPTENTRION

3

**parc du Chateau du Vert-Bois, 59700
Marcq-en-Barouel** (00) 33320462698

The Septentrion Foundation includes an interesting sculpture
park, some less interesting craft shops and this stiff and
underfrequented restaurant which, although surrounded by
motorways, gives the illusion of being in deepest country.
Potjevleish is a French-Flemish terrine of chicken, rabbit and
ham and it is the last which, unsurprisingly, predominates,
rendering it rather akin to jambon persille. It is served here with
disgraceful bread – a cottonwool wad – a pickled pear and a
salad so vinegary it hurts. Salmon is braised (poached, actually)
in beer and served with chicory that really has been braised.
This is sound enough. Maroilles is roast (Welsh rarebitted,
actually) with another salad intent on buccal assault. Beer ice
cream is served with chantilly flavoured by genever. You
couldn't get much more northern, but you could get a lot more
skilful.

L TUES TO SUN, D TUES, WED, FRI, SAT £60

L'ATLANTIC

6

Digue de Mer, 62930 Wimereux (00) 33321324101

From the first-floor dining room you can watch the sun go
down over the marine horizon. Inside the room you can watch
the lobster tank and get the measure of these crustaceans'
shocking behaviour. The cooking is pleasingly competent but
hardly startling. A copious portioned dish of oysters replaced in
the shell with blobs of caviar was marred by a cauliflower
puree, which was too bland to add much. Turbot was slightly
tough and wasn't much helped by an underpowered hol-
landaise. The wine list is decent.

L EVERY DAY, D MON TO SAT £70

NORMANDY

LE BISTROT DU CHEF EN GARE

5

place Bernard Tissot, 76000 Rouen (00) 33235714115

The chef in question is Gilles Tournadre, acknowledged as the
top man in town. This is his second restaurant. And second
restaurants are invariably the better bet – simplicity, value for
money, no fol de rol, etc. This first-floor establishment is
decorated with, inter alia, a large-scale model train, which holds
wine and railwayman's caps. Fine lisettes (tiny mackerels) in the
classic fashion with white wine and onions. Nice crab with mayo;
ditto duck confit and pommes salardaises; stringy but tasty veal
shank; wonderfully dense chcocolate mousse. First-rate sorbets.

£65+

CENTRAL FRANCE

AUVERGNE

HOSTELLERIE DU BEFFROY 6
26 rue Abbé-Blot, 63610 Besse-en-Chandesse
(00) 33473795008
Chef Thierry Legros – Fat Terry to his mates, no doubt – gets just about everything right, save the cumbersome triangular plates, which are hopelessly out of place in the polished, woody, unpretentious dining room. The food on them is delicious. Ombre chevalier is done with a freshwater fish stock and diced mountain ham; the Auvergnat dish pounti is spiced with nutmeg and cinnamon and served with a compôte of sweated onions and jambon cru. The cheeses are predictably fine, the desserts wildly elaborate.

L TUES TO SUN, D TUES TO SAT £75

HOTEL BEAUSEJOUR 9
route de Maurs, 15340 Calvinet (00) 33471499168
Louis-Bernard Puech, the chef and owner, is mostly faithful to the cooking of his native region Chataigneraie. Recommended: poached egg with couennes (unctuous pork rinds); foie gras terrine; veal with garlic and a reduction of the cooking juices; braised ham with trompettes de mort. Truffade, an upmarket version of aligot with herbs and green bacon, is delicious. This is an area of the most beguiling vernacular buildings and, evidently, chestnut groves.

L AND D MON TO SAT £55

LE BOUGNAT 6
29 rue des Chaussetiers, 63000 Clermont-Ferrand
(00) 33473363698
This place is doggedly Auvergnat. In a wood-fired oven, a well-practised chef turns out gallettes auvergnates, delicate pizza-like tarts whose base is akin to water biscuit, whose top comprises ham, saucisson, cantal, mushrooms and egg. Also: hot crisp pigs' ears in vinaigrette, smoked magret with walnuts, particularly fine tripous, pears and prunes poached in red wine, good sorbets, Chanturgue from Michel Bellard on the outskirts of the city.

£40

LE TERROIR

5

16 rue Prefecture, 63000 Clermont-Ferrand
(00) 33473374713

This is the only restaurant I've been to with board-marked concrete walls. A hospitable septuagenarian runs it with her equally congenial son. Their chef delivers Auvergnat dishes, delivers them well. There is no pretence, just proper food: mountain ham, a potee of salt pork, sausage, cabbage and carrots, lamb cutlets with truffade. The local cheeses are generously served and there is an interesting selection of wines from the Cotes d'Auvergne.

£36

HOTEL DU NORD

7

15120 Montsalvy (00) 33471492003

An unselfconsciously rustic dining room in this one-horse, two-hotel town. Good charcuterie to start: raw ham, three sorts of saucisson sec, a porky terrine. Then: a delicate and savoury roquefort feuillete; tiny sweet lamb cutlets and a potato gratin; disappointingly bland duck confit with crisp, garlicky potatoes. To drink: a half of Entraygues et du Fel, which you wouldn't necessarily bother with, were it not local, but nor would you find it.

L AND D EVERY DAY (CLOSED JAN–MARCH) £38

PRE BOSSU

4

43150 Moudeyres (00) 33471051070

A 30-year-old neo-vernacular house with crowstepped gables and thatch. Asparagus is served with the Belgian accompaniment of chopped boiled egg, as well as a fried quail egg and salmon eggs. A dish of salmon in a creamy bouillon-based sauce is waterzooi in all but name. There's a welcome lightness to most of the dishes but there is equally a lack of sureness about seasoning. The wines are nicely selected with a fine showing from the Rhone.

L SAT AND SUN, D EVERY DAY (EASTER–NOVEMBER ONLY) £70

BRASSERIE DU CASINO

5

4 rue Casino, 03200 Vichy (00) 33470982306

As brasseries go, this is a midget, and its menu, too, is that of a bistro. It is tremendously congenial and the cooking is simple and correct. Vichysoisse is ace, based on a light stock and a proper balance between leek and potato; veal sweetbreads with toasted hazelnuts and grilled veal kidney with grape-must mustard were both spot-on. Drink chilled St Pourcain and water from Chateldon, a burgh just south of Vichy with a chateau to die for.

L THURS TO TUES, D THURS TO SAT, MON AND TUES £50

BURGUNDY

BISTROT DES HALLES

3

10 rue Bannelier, 21000 Dijon (00) 33380499415
This is indeed beside the big central market. The style is
self-consciously retro – check tablecloths, 1900ish electoliers,
ancient enamel advertisements. The menu includes a gamey
pâté with amber jelly and cornichons; hot ham cooked on the
bone with saupiquet, red wine sauce spiked with vinegar, and
pilaf rice with white raisins.

£40

LE GRAND CAFÉ

3

5 rue du Chateau, 21000 Dijon (00) 33380307744
A Seventies take on art deco. Oeufs en meurette and an
andouillette from Troyes were satisfying, salade niçoise was
at least copiously served lamb chops were negligently cooked.

L AND D EVERY DAY £45

LAMELOISE

7

place d'Armes, Chagny, 71150 Saone-et-Loire
(00) 33385 876565
This restaurant in a banal Burgundian burgh, twinned with
Letchworth, has three Michelin stars, awarded for its diligent
pursuit of excess; well, I assume that's the case – it can't be for
the cooking which, while it achieves real heights, is prone also
to lapses of judgment. A veal chop spread with a herb ointment
was far too salty, sauced with a mouth-mugging veal reduction;
a fairly ordinary magret was perfectly competent. Ravioli
stuffed with truffles and potato puree was excellent. All the
sweet stuff is good.

£15

L'ESPERANCE

10

089450 Sain-Pere-Sous-Vezelay (00) 3386333910
One of the greats. Marc Meneau cooks peasant food from
heaven, refined, of course – but not that much. He makes
no attempt at pretty decoration and abhors multiple flavours.
Every dish is centripetal. It's as though nouvelle cuisine had
never happened. Lightness is not a paramount aim, indeed,
it's all pretty substantial stuff. Turbot is roast in veal stock and
sauced with veal jus and served with marrow bones; foie gras
is poached with white coco beans and pork rinds; veal fillet is
roast and dished up with a bittersweet caramel sauce and a tart
tatin of endives. Kromeskies, devised by the French chefs at
Russian court, are done here in a version the size of a stock
cube – a deep-fried exterior hides a centre of liquid foie gras.
Oysters are jellied in their shells; pineapple is roast with vanilla

pods and ginger – this is a phenomenal dessert. The house wines are the chef's own. The locality, on the edge of the Morvan, is beautiful.

L AND D MON TO WED, D WED TO MON £210+

LE PRE DES MARGUERITES

7

89450 Saint-Pere-sous-Vezelay (00) 3386332045

Marc Meneau's second restaurant, right accross the road from L'Esperance. It is not much to look at but the cooking is predictably excellent and good value for money. The repertoire is down-home gear done with panache: fromage de tête, jambon persille, braised beef with noodles, mirabelle tart, etc.

L AND D TUES TO SUN £40+

CENTRE

ABBAYE ST-AMBROIX

3

Hotel de Bourbon, 60 av Jean-Jaurès, 18000 Bourges (00) 33248708000

The room is magnificent. Room? Space. A presumably Jesuit ruin, all stone dentil cornices, capitals, pilasters and broken walls. The cooking is overworked by a chef who is so sweet-toothed he might be English: foie gras and caramelised pumpkin; roe deer, which was underhung in the new English way, pumpkin, which was undercooked. Lots of flash, little taste. Hence the Michelin star.

£200

RHONE ALPES

CAFE DES FEDERATIONS

2

8 rue Major-Martin, 69001 Lyon (00) 33478282600

Even Lyon can fail. An awful lot of effort is put into pandering to an Anglo-American notion of Frenchness – the patron's a philosopher, the waitresses are, 'ow you say, 'coquette', the gew-gaws include a clock in the shape of a ham and a cut-out of Miss Berger 1955 holding a bottle of that pastis. But little effort is put into the cooking. There are burnt croutons in a frissee salad, the charcuterie is meanly served and insipid, an andouillette was tired, a gratin dauphinoise patently warmed over. And, sure enough, the customers were tourists – Americans filling in their holiday log ('Was it thirty or forty minutes delay at the airport?') and Parisians making scathing remarks about Lyonnaise cooking.

L AND D MON TO FRI £30

CHEZ PAUL

8

11 rue Major-Martin, 69001 Lyon (00) 33478283583

The meek don't inherit the earth, merely their grandmother's bouchon – but what better fate? The people who run this place look happy. Their customers are their friends; there is no menu. Bowls are brought over, a sort of delivered buffet of: lentil salad, garlic sausage, jambon cru, fromage de tete, museau vinaigrette. Then: excellent saucisson chaud and a tete de veau. Then: St Felicien or tiny wild strawberries. The wine comes in deep-bottomed 46cl flasks: young Chiroubles in this instance.

£32

LE GARET

7

7 rue Garet 69001 Lyon (00) 33478281694

Maroon paint, heavy varnish, a tiny zinc, a wall of fridges, lug-gage racks, an ad-hoc air-conditioning system slung from a wall, white paper tablecloths. And, sure enough, it delivers. A huge pike quenelle is surprisingly light and the fish's delicate flavour is not swamped by the inevitable accompaniment of sauce Nantua. Tablier de sapeur is perfectly made – a thin, crisp coat of bread-crumbs covers the tripe, which is served with a mustardy sauce tartare. It's all restorative, tonic, and simple in the right way.

L AND D MON TO FRI £60

L'EST

8

Gare des Brotteaux, 14 place Jules-Ferry 69006 Lyon (00) 33437242526

The most recent of Paul Bocuse's brasseries in Lyon. It occupies a former railway station. So there is a cantilevered railway with model trains circulating the room. It is as eccentric and beguiling as Bocuse's great restaurant. It is luxury on the cheap. The simplest things - service, salads, grill – are done with minimum fuss and maximum correctness. Recommended: salad of foie gras, mache, haricots verts; steak tartare; grilled Charolais; a perfect St Marcellin; fabulous gaufres with hot chocolate sauce.

£65

LEON DE LYON

9

1 rue Pleney, 69001 Lyon (00) 33472101112

Waiters in brown leather aprons, sommeliers in black leather aprons, polished wood and bronzes. The peripheral mini-courses were of superlative quality: boudin noir tartlet, a sort of savoury pain perdu, tomato concasse with basil cream, mini-cakes and biscuits, choc truffles. Recommended: bread-crumbed pig's ears with a tour de force of recondite charcuterie – pig's trotter made into a warm sausage with pistachio and tiny cubes of foie gras; fine cheeses. Serious wines at serious prices.

L AND D MON TO SAT £110+

LA MEUNIERE

8

11 rue Neuve, 69001 Lyon (00) 33478286291

Probably the pick of Lyon's bouchons. The food is wonderful,
and it is served with a generosity that borders on the reckless.
A bowl of pork scratchings (ace) is followed by an entree of
saladiers and charcuteries including two sorts of terrine, raw
ham, parsleyed ham, cooked ham, five sorts of rosette, jesus,
etc., pork muzzle, calf's foot in jelly, cervelas, radishes with
butter, cold tripe, herrings with potato salad. Main courses
include an entire roast calf's kidney. Great.

L AND D TUES TO SAT £50

LA VOUTE (CHEZ LEA)

7

11 place Antonin Gourju, 69002 Lyon (00) 33478420133

The premises are smarter than the average bouchon's: caramel,
cream and pink in the French decorative style of the late
Forties. Immutable classics are served with a minimum of
fuss. Lightly cured sausage is poached in white wine and
accompanied by steamed potato. Gras double is fried with
parsley and served with an impeccable pommes paillasson.
Various beaujolais are available in 46cl bottles.

L AND D MON TO SAT £65

PAUL BOCUSE

10

69660 Collonges-au-Mont-d'Or (00) 33472429090

Paul Bocuse exceeds all expectations. He is the last and
greatest mère; he is the pope of the stove, the Aga Aga. As a
restaurateur he is a sort of Buñuel; he works magic; he creates
a weird world. This is the most eccentric joint imaginable.
The cooking is simple and magnificent. It is free of chi-chi
and pretence. This brigade is so supremely confident it doesn't
need to shout about it. Every dish is a gastronomic integrity,
every dish is copious, every dish is really the ideal version of
a dish that has been made in Lyons for years.

£200

L'ANCIENNE AUBERGE

10

01540 Vonnas (00) 33474509050

The ointment pink and turquoise building has been restored so
that it is an apparantly faithful reproduction of the restaurant
George Blanc's grandparents famously ran. There is no better
cooking in the world than that which elevates French rural
bourgeois practice of a century ago to the heavens without
compromising its essence. Dinner here was one of the best I've
eaten in my life: tripe in strips cooked in white wine, bread-
crumbed and gratinated; onion terrine; Bresse chicken cooked
in crème fraîche, wine and onions; chicken liver mousse; tarte
au sucre; chocolate cake. The serving staff are charming.

£170

ANDRE BARCET

19 bis cours Victor-Hugo, St-Etienne 42000
(00) 33477324363

6

The restaurant is rather dated (swagged, scumbled, marbled, ragged, peach and pink); the service is by a fellow anxious to break into light entertainment – blinding blue and black dogtooth jacket, funny shirt, bow tie. The cooking is not so ostentatious. Fried foie gras, asparagus and hunks of crustacean is a combination that doesn't really integrate; veal loin and breads are lacklustre, though lifted by the potato and egg galettes which are one of this city's rare specials.

L AND D EVERY DAY £75+

SOUTH EAST FRANCE

LANGUEDOC–ROUSILLON

LES DEMEURES DU RANQUET

rte de St-Hippolyte-du-Fort, 30140 Tournac
(00) 33466775163

9

The main building is an old mas, whose grounds are littered with mostly wooden sculptures. Anne Majorel is a fine chef whose dishes are wholly based in elegantly amended local custom and based on local produce – even a lobster has only 60km to come to meet its fate. Which is to be served with a sort of cake of pig's trotter. Best of all is shoulder of lechal lamb with a gratin that is akin to pommes Anna. The sweetness and ease of all this is signal. There is no chi-chi, no show, just total confidence.

L AND D EVERY DAY IN SUMMER £75+

PROVENCE COTE D'AZUR

NEAT

11 square Mérimée, 06400 Cannes (00) 33493992919

9

This is tantamount to treason: Joel Robuchon, THE French chef, has hailed as his successor an Englishman, un ros-bif, un angliche monolingue. But Neat is the works. He is deter-mined to keep alive the flame of haute cuisine and avoids the common pitfalls of overintensity and over-richness. Near-perfect pitch is consistently maintained: pig's head comprises fritters of tongue and brain and braised cheek; a fine pigeon ensemble includes pink breast and a charlotte of the pluck; tiny turbots of startling freshness are as sweet as they come. The wine, list created by Bruno Asselin, is lovely.

L AND D MON TO SAT £120; SET LUNCH £55+

CHEZ FONFON

9

140 vallon des Auffes, 13007 Marseille (00) 33491521438

The vallon des Auffes is a tiny cove dominated by the corniche bridge high above it. Further east along the coast it would be tarted up and bougainvillaea'd. But this is Marseille, so it's all pre-prettification and likely to remain so. This is a tight, neat establishment, whose kitchen mostly restricts itself to grilling over wood, cooking in a salt crust and turning out impeccable fish stews. Bourride is done in the immemorial fashion: broth thickened with aioli, a variety of fish (red mullet, conger, bream, John Dory, etc.) on a separate plate, rusk-like croutons, big bowls of aioli and rouille. This is splendid. So is a lemon soufflé containing zest and candied fruit. Recommended.

L AND D TUES TO SAT £65+

PATALAIN

6

49 rue Sainte, 13001 Marseille (00) 33491550278

The basement is a nightclub straight out of J-P Melville. The ground-floor dining room is 'inspired' by art-nouveau – ogee-shaped mirrors, bizarre veneers, strange wallpaper. The ur-Provençal pieds et paquets is raised to real heights: the lamb tripe is stuffed with a persilade and muscle meat, the lamb feet are going on gelatinous and the white wine/tomato sauce is excellently piquant. Brains and tongue are done in a sort of fricassee with onions, carrots, peppercorns, capers and vinegar. Toasted goat's cheese with mesclun is a cut above the normal.

L TUES TO FRI, D TUES TO SAT £70

SOUTH WEST FRANCE

AQUITAINE

LA MAMOUNIA

5

51 rue la Faurie-de-Monbadon, 33000 Bordeaux
(00) 33556812184

A tented room, a fountain, fretted wood, microtonic music. The visual and aural decor are off-the-peg; the north African cooking is rather better than that. The salad of cold cooked toma-toes, peppers, cumin and turmeric, called mechonia, is delicious; couscous is served with the usual grilled meats and the unusual addition of pickled grapes and chickpeas. Otherwise: brik; tagine of mutton (not lamb) with prunes and almonds; and pastilla, the sugared meat pie (here, filled with chicken), which is the source of so much southwestern pastry – hence the word pastis (not the drink). There's a lightish red from Meknes called Guerrouan, which is better than the Moroccan norm.

L EVERY DAY, D SUN TO FRI £45

LA TUPINA 11
6 rue Porte de la Monnaie, 33000 Bordeaux
(00) 33556915637
The best restaurant in the world. Jean-Pierre Xiradakis is
sedulously faithful to the customs and repertoire of Bx and
its environs. He shuns refinement and abhors novelty. The
restaurant is self-consciously rustic but done with discretion –
though in the corridor to the toilet a tiny speaker emits farmyard
noises. When you enter you are confronted with a vast fireplace
and a log fire and a bizarre arrangement of spits, pans, hooks
and chains. The cooking is unremittingly carnal: several breeds
of beef are offered, along with pork chitterlings, lamb tripe,
sanguette (a sort of chicken blood omelette), jambom cru,
garbure, spitroast partridge with braised cabbage, lamprey,
chips cooked in duck fat. Duck fat is ubiquitous. Amiable,
unfussy service. This is what all restaurants should be like.

L AND D MON TO SAT £90+

MIDI PYRENEES

L'ESPRIT DU VIN 9
11 quai Choiseul, 81000 Albi (00) 33563546044
The terrace inhabits a truly beguiling site that looks up to the
awesome structure of Albi cathedral. The chef, Patrick Maury,
possesses high craft, tempered invention, exquisite taste. Duck
confit is done with a sweet-sour sauce of real delicacy; tiny
mackerel are salted and weighted in a terrine which is truly
great; lamb is slow-cooked for five hours but first browned so
that a crust forms. The place is run with charm and spirit.

L TUES TO SUN, D TUES TO SAT £70+

LA RESERVE 4
route de Cordes, 81000 Albi (00) 33563476022
A swish hotel beside a sluggish reach of the Tarn. It's the kind
of place where the waiter scowls at you if you dare to pour your
own wine. The chef can cook, but he so persistently shoots himself in the foot with silly little garnishes that it's a wonder he's
still standing. A croustillant of salt cod certainly didn't require an
accompaniment of beetroot puree. A half leg of duck confit with
the other half made into a parmentier is proper gear – but it was
decorated with inedible dried tomato skins. Veal rib is all right.

L AND D EVERY DAY (CLOSED IN WINTER) £70+

LA TAVERNE LE BOURG

3

81150 Castelnau-de-Levis, Albi (00) 33563609016

An ill-named restaurant that is nothing like a tavern; it is pretentious and preposterously out of place. Dishes are served under domes by tyro staff clearly not at home with these devices. Foie gras terrine and foie gras pâté is served, incredibly, with a very sweet ice cream; a pigeon and cep salad is marred by the fungi being slightly burnt. Cheeses and a crème brûlée are outstandingly good.

L AND D TUES TO SAT £80+

LA TETE DE L'ART

2

7 rue de la Piale, 81000 Albi (00) 33563384475

A cheapish outfit to the south of Albi cathedral, where the waiters dress like extras from Borsalino. It plays nonstop chansons and names its menus after Nougaro, Brel, etc. Tripes a l'albigeoise tasted as though they might have come out of a tin; entrecote and duck magret is properly fresh and competently done.

L AND D EVERY DAY £40+

HOTEL DES VOYAGEURS

9

1 av de Rodez, 12290 Pont-de-Salars
(00) 33565468308

This is everything that can be demanded of a restaurant: time-honoured recipes, first-class ingredients, cooked with attention and served by an amiable staff. The various dry sausages, charcuterie and hams with which lunch begins are of stellar quality. Coq au vin is made properly, with cockerel that has been long marinated; crème caramel and chocolate mouse is absolutely proper.

L MON TO SUN, D MON TO SAT £35

LA DILIGENCE,

6

On N140 at 12330 Nuces (00) 33565726020

The service at this pretty place doesn't live up to its name; it is, rather, dilatory. The cooking, however, is correct, simple, unadorned and to the point. A truffle omelette is lightly souffléd and the quality of the eggs is ace. Foie gras is fried in massive portions and given a dressing of capers. Exceptional duck confit comes with duchesse potatoes. Eat in the garden and watch buzzards on thermals over the red bluffs nearby.

L AND D EVERY DAY £40

L'Eau Vive: Hotel Moderne   4
27 bd de Guizard, 12500 Espalion (00)3 3565440511
The hotel was indeed modern in about 1890. It seems to
belong to some indefinable yesterday. The speciality is
supposedly freshwater fish. Ombre chevalier is a relation of
char. It was over-cooked with a well-made sauce of hazelnuts,
onions and cream. The fresh salmon in a salad was also overcooked. Salted lamb ham is for the curious. The light red wine
from the next town along the Lot, Estaing, is acceptable.

L AND D EVERY DAY £35+

Hotel carayon   3
place du Fort, 12380 St-Sernin-sur-Rance
(00) 33565996026
An infinitely expanded inn that is a shrine to the owners and
their perma-tans. Characterful Pierre and vivacious Claudette
stare out of countless photos, some of them a metre square
and mounted on lightboxes. The menu looks good, but dish
after dish is remarkable for its inaccuracy and clumsiness.
Untrimmed foie gras in a separating sauce; insipid stuffed
cabbage; flavourless entrecote. The cheese trolley is a drop-in
centre for every fly for miles around.

L EVERY DAY, D MON TO SAT £55+

Le Mejane   6
8 rue Mejane, 12500 Espalion (00) 33565482237
The decor is heartsinking. It's a showroom of mirror finishes,
veneers, ebonising, paint effects. The cooking also has
pretensions, but is at least founded on sound technique and
doesn't get too fussy. Pig's foot is mixed with remoulade and
served with a 'cake' of brioche dough, into which are incorpo-
rated pieces of pig's ear. First-rate beef comes with a slightly
truffled sauce; lamb's breads are done with onions; hot chocolate tart is splendid.

L THURS TO TUES, D MON, TUES, THURS TO SAT £55+

Le Vieux Pont   9
12390 Belcastel (00) 33565655229
Named for the packhorse bridge across the Aveyron in this
near-vertical village of stunning prettiness. The sisters who
own it possess the sort of understated metropolitan taste that
is rare among French provincial hoteliers. Cod with pureed
rocket was knockout stuff; 'cake' of ceps and lardons was
served with greaseless rabbit rillettes; gigot came with a
sweetbread brochette; beef with a gratin of potato and
roquefort. The cooking is marked by a perfect balance.

L TUES TO SUN, D TUES TO SAT (CLOSED JAN AND FEB) £60

LA BALANDRE

3

Hotel Terminus, 5 av de Ch-de-Freycinet, 46000 Cahors
(00) 33565350766
Another instance of a smalltown restaurant essaying
metropolitan chic and getting it wrong. The restaurant is
characterised by stiff, gauche, predominantly adolescent
service; by laborious and inaccurate cooking. But lurking in
the kitchen is a patissier/confectioner who is blessed with
a true gift. A sweet tomato confit – the fruit is steeped in
sugar but not turned glace – was stuffed with dried fruits
and peel and served with a geranium ice cream. Massive
selection of Cahors wines.

£120+

HOTEL DE FRANCE

7

2 place de la Liberation, 32003 Auch (00) 33562617171
The cooking at this celebrated hotel is an uneasy mix of rustic
and posh, but the foie gras is recommended.

L AND D EVERY DAY £110, SET MENU FROM £40

LA RAPIERE

5

32120 Mauvezin (00) 3362068008
Pleasant village inn decorated with murderous-looking farm
tools and hanging baskets. The clientele is composed of
front-row forwards. Some of the dishes hit the spot – ceps
fried with parsley and garlic, tender duck breast with a truffle
sauce and gratin dauphinois. Tete de veau, chopped into bite-
size pieces, is less pleasing and is mugged with an over-
acidulated vinaigrette.

L THURS TO TUES, D THURS TO MON £35+

POIDS PUBLIC

8

31540 St Felix Lauragais (00) 33561830020
Stonewalled dining room in a fortified hill village. The
well-pitched cooking is not slavishly regional but includes
a first-class cassoulet.

L AND D EVERY DAY £75

AUGUY

9

2 allée de l'Amicale 12210 Laguiole (00) 33565443111
The dining room is all orange paint and limed oak dado.
Jean-Marie Muylaert runs the place with some élan. His wife,
Isabelle, is a wonderful cook: her repertoire is sedulously
regional, executed with a precision and a rejection of percieved
ideas that set her apart. A galette of pig's trotter wrapped in
raw ham was ace; the aligot was exemplary; charred grilled faux
fillet tasted the way beef should, but so infrequently does.

Great cheeses as befits the Aveyron. Drink Philippe Teulie's
Domaine de Cros.

L AND D EVERY DAY IN SUMMER; L TUES TO SUN, D TUES TO SAT
REST OF YEAR £45

HOTEL L'AUBRAC

5

17 allée de l'Amicale, 12210 Laguiole (00) 33565443213
Right across the road from the outstanding, and much more
expensive, Auguy. The 60FF menu (£6, 9 euro) is an
astonishing bargain: tripous, stuffed cabbage, copious cheese,
pichet of house wine (Entraygues et du Fel).

£25

LE ROCHER DE L'ARSAULT

7

15 rue l'Arsualt, 24000 Perigueux (00) 33553535406
Old-fashioned, ur-provincial, semi-troglodytic premises built
into the low cliff beside the river Isle and run with great charm
by the Leymarie sisters: Marie cooks, Valerie waits. There are
photos of truffle pigs on the walls and truffles in every other
dish. A truffle cooked in meat sauce under a pastry dome was
lovely. So, too, was a deafeningly yellow truffle omelette.
Tournedos rossini included truffle and ceps; duck confit is
done with ceps.

£100+

LE BROUSSY

2

Hotel Broussy, 1 av Victor-Hugo, 12000 Rodez
(00) 33565681871
This art deco prodigy across the square from the awesome
red sandstone cathedral is worthwhile in more than a faute
de mieuxish way. The cafe part, under separate ownership, is
seedy; the restaurant and hotel merely gently distressed; food
and wine are unselfconsciously regional: charcuterie, tripous,
aligot, magret, roquefort, lacandou and Marcillac.

£35

LA TAVERNE

9

23 rue de l'Embergue, 12000 Rodez (00) 33564421451
This place is a gem. Jean-Louis Pomerade is a scrupulous
enthusiast for Aveyronnais country cooking as well as being a
delightful host. His backstreet bistro is beamed, roughcast,
tongue and groove. It is cramped and highly animated. Farcou
is a paste of chopped chard, onion, parsley, garlic and diced
pork, fried in quoits the size of a burger: this is heavenly
cooking. Confit duck is served in epic proportions with an
intensely garlicky aligot. The bread, cheeses and simple
desserts are top-notch.

£32

CARMEN: RESTAURANT DES ABATTOIRS   5
7 allée Charles-de-Fitte, Toulouse (00) 33561420495
Teetotal vegetarians steer well clear. The walls are hung
with photos depicting hard-core abattoir action. There are
tessellated representations of kine. The place is cramped and
packed out with a mix of businessmen, smart women shoppers,
blue collars, layabouts. Everyone drinks copiously and eats
vastly: numerous cuts of steak; duck magret with wonderful
potatoes fried with smoked bacon, onion, parsley and garlic;
stuffed lamb tripe in tomatoe sauce; cold boiled beef with
salad. The cooking is a bit hit and miss, but it's a hugely
enjoyable place where the pleasure is manifestly guilt-free.
Young wines are more than adequate. The geniality is catching.

L TUES TO SAT, D MON TO SAT £35+

LES JARDINS DE L'OPERA   7
1 place du Capitole, 31000 Toulouse (00) 33561230776
It takes five Toulogains to open, sniff, taste and decant a bottle
of wine. The decor is hideous; the pretentious formality risable.
When the chef resists overelaboration the food is splendid:
ceps roasted with bone marrow and garlic; a thin-based pear
tart; raviolis stuffed with foie gras and sauced with truffle butter. But a cassoulet based on broad beans is refined to the point
at which it is no longer a cassoulet. Duck is not enhanced by
tarragon butter. The prices are as ludicrous as the chi-chi.

L AND D MON TO SAT £150+, SET MENUS FROM £65

GERMANY

BAVARIA

AM KRANEN   5
Am Kranenkai 1, Wurzburg (00) 4993150130
Wurzburg combines wine and the baroque. This delightful
riverside restaurant is attached to the headquarters of the
Franconian Winegrowers' Association. It is a good place to
sample those wines, which include some estimable reds from
nearby Randersacker. The service is charming and the simple
food is diligently prepared. Radish soup is a revelation. Also
recommended: eels in sage cream; cep soup; rump steak
with creamed ceps.

£55+

GEIGER 7

Stanggass, Berchtesgaden (00) 4986529653

1890s chalet that owes more to the American 'shingle style'
than to Alpine vernacular. It is an individualistic hotel with a
restaurant that uses local produce in a satisfying way. Ceps
are fried or served with noodles and cream.; duck is done with
damsons – this is good enough to convert those who shy away
from fruit with meat; pigeon, rabbit and venison are served
with a mushroom fricassee; veal is done with an outstanding
white-truffle risotto. Cheeses are all from the mountains that
surround the small town. Good puddings, fairly priced wines.

£70

GLOCKENBACH 8

Kapuzinerstrasse 29, Munich (00) 4989534043

The French co-owner Michel Dupuis is a former sommelier,
and the wine list of this converted 'pub' shows it; there is first-
rate gear from Daumas Gassac, Clape and Ott – and prices are
modest (by German standards). The other owner, Karl Ederer,
is a talented chef, whose debt to his native cuisine is mercifully slight. Top-notch dishes include poached beef (a la ficelle in
all but name and lack of string) with spinach ravioli, asparagus
and fried ceps; boudin noir with steamed vegetables in a butter
sauce; raw tuna with rocket. Ederer has the lightest of touches,
buys fine ingredients and does not hide their flavours with an
excess of conceits. Puddings are good, cheeses are French.

CLOSED MON £70

GOLDENES POSTHORN 3

Glockleingasse 2, Nuremberg (00) 49911225153

Ancient oil paintings of guilds, sound Franconian wines, gutsy
cooking which, while it is much finer than the German norm,
is still not for the faint-hearted. Ceps are done in cream with
dumplings; venison is served in gargantuan portions, having
been cooked with fruit and possibly chocolate.

CLOSED SUN (EXCEPT FOR PARTIES) £65

HALALI 3

Schonfeldstrasse 22, Munich (00) 4989285909

Brown panelling and antlers. Brawn is not helped by the
inclusion of smoked meat that overpowers the unsmoked;
venison is nicely cooked; so is the beef with a horse-radish
crust. Ravioli stuffed with ceps and duck are served in a
pleasing cep butter sauce, but the pasta is woeful.

L AND D MON TO FRI, SAT D £30, A LA CARTE £30–£40

KREUTZER
8
Badstrasse 54, Oberon Worhd, Regensburg
(00) 4994188711
Regensburg is an unusually well-preserved town – that is to
say, Bomber Command took out its target, a Messerschmidt
factory, but not much else. The centre is gothic and is surrounded by villas in parks, like Cheltenham. This fine, small
restaurant is on an island between two branches of the
Danube. The chef, Detlev Schmidkunz, and his Dutch wife
seem to run it by themselves. Some of the cooking is absolutely excellent. Homemade black pudding is fried between slices
of roesti; lamb is roasted with a coriander-seed crust; damsons
are stewed and served with damson ice cream and a sort of
madeleine. Good wines.

£100+

TANTRIS
3
Johann-Fichte-Strasse 7, Munich (00) 49893619590
Ludicrous prices, ludicrous decor, ludicrous pretension. This
is where Munich gets dressed up. The result is a Bet Lynch
lookalike contest. The place recalls a sophisticated disco in
Alderley Edge c. 1980. The sommelier's pompous ritual has to
be seen to be believed. Yet much of the cooking is impressive:
ravioli stuffed with calf's head and garnished with sweetbreads
in a tomato sauce; beef cheek with marrowbone dumplings in
a well-gauged reduction sauce; cherry tarte fin with almond
ice cream. A veal chop was bland. Wines are excessively dear.

£200

BERLIN

LE GRAND SILHOUETTE
6
Maritim Grand Hotel, Friedrichstrasse, 158-64
(00) 493020335
Preposterous repro art-nouveau decor, startlingly grabby prices,
battalions of waiters, choreographed dome-lifting, live music –
well, musicians who breathe, anyway. The cooking is highly
accomplished and marred only by the thought of the damage.
Deep-fried calf's head is served with (pointless) pieces of
lobster and a terrific cep sauce and light sage dumplings;
sweetbreads with white truffle sauce and pasta are delicious,
if on the hefty side; beef is done in a red wine reduction. Big
selection of French cheeses.

L EVERY DAY, D FRI TO SAT, BUFFET £10 TO £25

Maritim Hotel

6

Hollerallee 99, Bremen (00) 4942137890

This chain of hotels employs chefs who know what they're
doing (see also Berlin). Of course the cooking is 'international',
but that is to be welcomed after most German cooking. The
Muzak and the decor are bland; the food isn't: duck livers with
deep-fried onions and sweetish fried apples; sweetbreads in a
sort of sabayon sauce with chanterelles and root veg; calf's
head terrine with tomato sauce. Overpriced wines.

£100+

Zur Goldene Gans

4

Maritim Grand Hotel, Friedrichstrasse 148-46
(00) 493023270

Singlemindedly devoted to its titular bird. Goose legs, goose
breast, goose offal, goose soup, goose fat – which is served
with bread, or used to cream curly cale.

£60

Schleswig-Holstein

Schiffergesellschaft

7

Breite Strasse 2, Lubeck (00) 4945176776

An absolute must –not on account of the Holsteiner
specialities, even though these are both interesting and
delicious, but because of the sheer beauty and eccentricity of
the premises. Lubeck is a beguiling place, the former capital
of the Hanseatic League. Its architecture, then, has affinities
with such distant ports as Stralsund and Bruges. This house
might have been lifted from the latter. It is of the mid-16th
century, has lavish crowstep gables and an amazing interior,
which commemorates its initial existence as a merchant sea
captain's guild house. There are vast models of galleons slung
from the beams, high-backed settles, scrubbed tables 20m
long, copper chandeliers. It is immensely popular with locals.
There is nothing precious about it. The repertoire includes the
dish labskaus – which is how scousers got their name: it was
brought back from the Baltic by Liverpudlian sailors. It
comprises a spiced puree of potatoes and meat with a salted
herring on the side and a fried egg on top. Another local
winner is pickled potted duck – an entire boned duck served
in its jelly in a Kilner jar. Lubeck would make a good weekend
destination – it's 45 minutes from Hamburg.

£50

ITALY

NAPLES

BELLINI
6

Via Constantinopoli, 79 (00) 39081459774

The restaurant is on two floors, grey-tiled with an open kitchen and a small terrace. The deep-frying – of small octopi with their ink sacs intact, of big octopi, langoustines, aubergines, potato and ham croquettes, and rice balls – is first-class. And the pizza with (more) octopus, mussels and clams is the best I tasted in the city.

L MON TO SUN AND D MON TO SAT £35+

LA BERSAGLIERA
4

Borgo Marinaro, 10 (00) 390817646016

The habitual Italian talent for juxtaposition of disparate architectural and decorative manners deserted whoever it was that devised this balls-up. A perfectly sound and lavish 1900 interior has been marred by a terrible Sixties extension. If you turn your back on this, it is really rather good: big mirrors, neo-rococo bacchanals, energetically carved wood – plus ancient waiters and competent and typically cautious cooking. Mozzarella in carrozza is hefty but rice croquettes stuffed with eggs and ham are pleasant enough. Drink Fiano de Avellino, of which La Bersagliera has several vintages – it is quite atypical of Italian whites, that's to say, it's pretty good.

L AND D WED TO MON £46+

DA MIMI
6

Via Alfonso d'Aragona, 21 (00) 390815538525

Da Mimi, aka Mimi al Ferrovia, is all pale wood, cream paint, spruce tiles. The waiters are highly trained jobsworths – but at least they're as charmlessly brusque to evident regulars as they are to more casual punters. Not that there are many of the latter: it is constantly booked out, off-limits to passers by. It's popularity is partly due to the excellence of its pasta e ceci. And no wonder. It is as fine and savoury a creation as you could wish for. I can only assume it is not more widely offered because of its appearance – grey/green/khaki. Da Mimi also does a competent fritto misto of seafood and it serves an artisanal mozzarella which makes you see the point of that frequently industrialised cheese.

L AND D MON TO SAT £35+

DON SALVATORE   7
Via Mergellina, 5 (00) 39081681817

Don Salvatore is close to the sea in the suburb of Mergellina and
is run with abundant amiability. The wines are good and the cooking is excellent. Gnocchi are served with clams and courgette
flowers; porcini are grilled with garlic and olive oil. The bread is
thin pizza bread. Minced sardines are made into the most delicious fritters; ice creams are served like petits fours in fairy cake
cases – the flavours are various, the high standard is constant.

L AND D THURS TO TUES £45+

UMBERTO   3
Via Alabardieri, 30 (00) 39081418555

There are bold chandeliers, lots of red leather and bentwood.
It's a place where the lower bourgeoisie lets its hair down,
loudly. A guitarist wanders from table to table singing
sentimental songs. He's no Gigli, and, besides, he's drowned
out by the laughter and screams. The cooking is run of the
mill. Frittura and pizza are all right.

L AND D TUES TO SUN £25+

ROME

AGATA E ROMEO   5
Via Carlo Alberto, 45 (00) 39064466115

Nuova cucina is alive here; whether it's altogether well is another
matter. Three soups of different densities, spinach, pumpkin and
bean are served in the same dish, unmixed. Clever, but pointless.
Pasta has basil and cheese in the mix and is served with pulped
raw tomato. Swordfish is also served raw; sturgeon is sauced with
pancetta and red wine. The service is flashy, slightly pretentious.

£133

AL POMPIERE   5
Via Santa Maria Dei Calderari, 38 (00) 39066868377

Jewish, it serves pig in the form of prosciutto. A first-floor
establishment close to the synagogue. It serves a sound mixed
fry of salt cod, artichoke hearts and cougettes. The duodenum
dish called 'pajata' is particularly good. Offal is served with
rigatoni in a spiced tomato sauce.

MON TO SAT £35

LA CARBONARRA

5

Campo Dei Fiori, 23 (00) 39066864783

Chaotic, multi-storey outfit with rude waiters, which is rare
in Rome. The tripe here is exceptional even in a city devoted
to that offal. It is cooked in the standard manner, with tomato,
mint and orange, but with unusual finesse. Bang next door to
the Farnese Palace.

WED TO MONDAY £50

CHECCHINO DAL 1887

10

Via Monte Testaccio (00) 39065746318

A remarkable and, evidently, ancient place. The restaurant
occupies a long tunnel-vaulted room opposite the old abattoirs
in an area now more celebrated for its gay clubs. The cooking
of Roman specialities, most of them offal dishes, is
impeccable. Veal head is done like a sublime brawn; there's a
marvellous mixed grill of sweetbreads, testicles, spinal cord,
duodenum and liver, each item lightly and differently spiced.
Spleen, heart and lungs are also available. The artisanal
cheeses are outstanding. The wine list is, unusually for Rome,
pan-Italian and very good indeed. There are numerous rare
amari. Service is endlessly courteous.

TUES TO SAT £65

COLLINE EMILIANE

9

Via Degli Avignonesi, 22 (00) 39064817538

First-class Bolognese and Modenese cooking in a backstreet
outfit near the Piazza Barberini. It looks like the interior of
some nightmarish ski-lodge. The bollito misto includes uncured
beef, tongue, osso bucco, calf's cheek, trotter. It is excellent
and so is the salsa verde with it. Veal is cooked in milk and is
served with a splendid parmesan flavoured potato puree. In
autumn, ceps are straightforwardly roasted with ceps and garlic.

SAT TO THURS £40

IL CARDINALE

6

Via Dei Carceri, 6 (00) 39066869336

The trad Roman bean and barley soup is well done here and so
too are carpaccio and oxtail with celery and tomato. There are a
number of (understandably) little-known Lazio wines to be had.

L AND D MON TO SAT £35

NINO

6

Via Borgnona, 11 (00) 39066795676

Sober panelled dining room, courteous waiters, sound
bourgeois cooking: bean soup, the vegetable and bechamel
mould called 'sformiato', ceps, grilled meats.

MON TO SAT £50

OTELLO

4

Via Croce, 81 (00) 39066791178

Immensely popular restaurant in a courtyard near the Spanish
Steps. The cooking can be rough, though the fry of brains and
courgettes is good. Also, rabbit roasted with peppers, stuffed
aubergine, veal stew.

MON TO SAT £25

PERILLI

3

Via Marmorata, 39 (00) 39065742415

Bustling outfit well out of the city centre and frequented by
local bourgeoisie. The cooking is as rough as the murals and
trompe l'oeil brickwork. Tripe is over-cheesed, ceps are soggy,
sweetbreads overcooked. Obliging staff; palatable house wine.

£45

SICILY

LE CAPRICE

3

Via Panoramica dei Templi 51, Agrigento
(00) 39092226469

The restaurant looks onto the celebrated Greek ruins. Cooking is
inconsistent. Antipasti include sardines in a sweet and sour marinade, frittata, plump anchovies – all these were unexceptionable;
but lamb cutlets were appalling – gristle, fat, bone, and rank meat.

SAT TO THURS £40

LEON D'ORO

7

Viale Emporium, San Leone, Agrigento
(00) 390922414400

The skilled kitchen in this seaside suburb demonstrates what
a terrific dish involtini can be: this version used raw ham as
a casing for ground veal with mozzarella in the centre. The
caponata was good. Mixed hot seafood comprised cockles,
mussels, stewed squid; mixed grilled meat – beef, veal, pork
sausage, meatball – was of high quality; green salad was
dressed with the loveliest oil, from Casa Montalbano.

TUES TO SUN £45

ARCHIMEDE

4

Via Mario Gemellaro 8, Siracusa (00) 39093169701

This place follows the fairly popular practice of offering
antipasti on a buffet: peperonata, marinated anchovies, stuffed
mussels, etc. This was followed by a mixed grill of fish.

MON TO SAT £30

DARSENA
5

Via Riva Garibaldi 6, Siracusa (00) 39093166104

The restaurant on the fishing harbour stares across a narrow
strip of water to the customs house and coastguard headquarters.
Grilled squid was particularly tender.; pasta was sauced with
tomato and, presumably, veal. The service is particularly amiable.

THURS TO TUES £35

DON CAMILLO
7

Via Maestranza 96, Siracusa (00) 39093167133

The top place in town. Rabbit fillets are roasted and sauced
with vegetables done in agrodolce (the emphasis is on the
dolce). It is delicious and light. Frittura goes beyond the
habitual squid and prawns to include bass and crab; the
egg in a stracciatella is omelette-like, the broth is Sicilian
penicillin; fritters of fry are the total works.

£30

LA FOGLIA
5

Via Capodieci 29, Siracusa (00) 39093166233

It looks like a junk shop run by indiscriminate hippies. Peeling
distemper, petrified cacti, old putti, etc. The cooks and waiters
are women. There is a bias toward vegetables and pulses. The
specifically Sicilian soup called 'maccu' is almost a puree and
is to be preferred to a chickpea soup. Stuffed and breaded
sardines were skilfully prepared.

MON TO SUN £35

JONICO
6

Riviera Dionisio il Grande 194, Siracusa (00) 39093165540

Perched above a rocky cove in the city's outskirts, the
establishment does not rely on its spectacular position. It
has more to offer: amiable hospitality and precise cooking.
Antipasti were exemplary and unafraid of piquancy. Also
worth the trip: spaghetti al muddo. The pasta is served with
a winning combination of pounded anchovies and fried
breadcrumbs.

£35

MINERVA
4

Piazza Duomo 20, Siracusa (00) 39093169404

A big bourgeois canteen opposite the baroque façade of the
duomo. The menu is straightforward, execution is polished,
portions vast. Peperonata is made here with green peppers,
green olive oil and sweet onions; fritto misto is greaseless.

TUES TO SUN £25

LA RAMBLA

3

Via dei Mille 8, Siracusa (00) 39093166638

Housed in Siracusa's only essay in the neo-gothic – a cherry-red building of singular theatricality – beside the fishing harbour. Fritto misto is competently made. With it, a rocket salad. Also: pizza with ham, preserved mushrooms and hard-boiled egg.

MON TO SUN £15

LA SICILIANA

3

Via Savoia 17, Siracusa (00) 39093168944

A charmingly run outfit frequented by blue-collar families in large parties. The food is downhome stuff cooked with more enthusiasm than accuracy. A brown bean soup was certainly well-flavoured, but was also very heavy indeed; tripe with potato, celery and carrots was leaden and bland. A 50cl flask of more than acceptable house wine is a giveaway at about £1.50.

TUES TO SUN £20

SPAIN

ZORTZIKO

8

Alameda de Mazarredo 17, Bilbao (00) 34944239743

Generically close to what you'd get at more or less any Michelin-starred restaurant outside France: perpetually repeated show tunes and boudoir-from-hell 1980s French decor. The menu displays a photo of chef Daniel Garcia looking pleased with himself. But then he as every right to do so: lobster with a risotto 'cake' and an intense tomato 'gazpacho', and grilled foie gras with slices of fig, ceps and broad beans were as good as they come. Pigeon and duck were slightly spoiled by overpowering, over-reduced sauces. The meat was unimpeachable in both cases. A 1970 CVNE Imperial Gran Reserva is among the best dollops of wallop I've had for a long time.

L AND D MON TO SAT £70

CASA OJEDA

5

Victoria 5, Burgos (00) 3494720982

Part-shop, part-bar, part-garden, part-restaurant. The last is on the first floor, and is agressively furnished in the 'Castillian style'. Lots of brown wood, heraldic escutcheons, beaten metal, leather. Lamb's sweatbread with 'young garlies' was not bad at all; raw ham was as good as ever; a red bean soup with black pudding was monotonous. Cheeses include three vintages of Burgos, which is sometimes made with ewe's milk, sometimes with goat's, sometimes with a mix of the two.

L EVERY DAY, D MON TO SAT £52+

MESÓN DE LOS INFANTES

6

Corral de los Infantes, Burgos (00) 34947205982

The restaurant occupies a corner of an alley which is strung with washing. Suckling pig is more than acceptable: crisp skin, pale, tender meat – and that's it, save for a very little jus and excellent chips. Before this: jabugo ham – the best ham in the world – and slightly battered squid of astonishing freshness. Service is leisurely, the house wine friendly enough.

L AND D EVERYDAY £32+

DUQUE CERVANTES

7

Segovia 12, Caceres (00) 34921462487

Segovia is among the most startlingly sited towns in Europe, and among the most beautiful, too. Its Roman aqueduct is a marvel of civil engineering. The place's gastronomic reputation rests on its suckling pigs and it seems generally agreed that Duque has the edge over its competitors in roasting these animals to a perfect crispness. The house also offers first-class tapas of tuna empanadilla, morcilla and ham croquettes. Good-quality steak is served with crisp chips. White beans come in two services – the first with a tomato sauce, the next as a basis for a sort of fabada of dried morcilla, ox muzzle, chorizo and salted pork

L AND D EVERY DAY £20–£25

EL FIGON DE EUSTAQUIO

4

Plaza de San Juan, Caceres (00) 34927248194

Just outside the walls of the old town and supposedly the best of the joints that offer Extremeno cooking; not bad, but far from special. Mijas comprises fried bread with, in this case, an egg on top; frito is not fried, but slow-cooked lamb with an overdose of pimenton. The cheese called Tortas del Casar is nasty. Spain, like Britain, should leave soft cheeses to the French.

L AND D EVERY DAY £35

EL FARO

8

San Felix 15, Cadiz (00) 34956211068

A great fish restaurant – big, old, stylish, which serves impeccable and often highly original dishes. Eggs are scrambled in the manner of piperade but with prawns and mushrooms; elvers are done with chilli and garlic; there are fine shellfish croquettes with cockles and garlic. Hake is served with a raw tomato and olive oil sauce.

L AND D EVERY DAY £35

LA BOLA

7

Bola 5, Madrid (00) 34915476930

Traditional Madrileño cooking in two dining rooms divided by a half-exposed kitchen. Cocido comes in two stages. First, the broth with vermicelli, then the simmered meats – beef, chicken and chorizo, plus potatoes and chickpeas; it is a less sophisticated version of pot au feu or bollito misto, but delicious nonetheless. Also worth trying: battered baby squids and a perfectly grilled sole. Nice desserts include cold apple fritters and oranges in orujo, a white brandy. Service is exceptionally accommodating.

L MON TO SAT, D MON TO FRI £20

TERETE

10

Lucrecia Arana 17, Haro, Rioja (00) 34941303220

A very fine restaurant that has been in business for 120 years. There are two dining rooms: an upstairs, where the tables are worn-down butcher's blocks, and a half-timbered downstairs which is slightly more soigné. Its reputation is based upon lamb: precisely, upon lechal lamb, very slowly roasted. Larry comprised crisp skin and meat; that's all save for a very small amount of cooking juice. He is habitually eaten with (very good) chips or lettuce salad. There are three vintages of house rioja – the oldest is from 1978 and worth a punt at £12.

L TUES TO SUN, D TUES TO SAT £30+

LAS BATUECAS

5

La Alberca, Salamanca (00) 34923415188

A bloated stone chalet in the largest village in the breathtaking Sierra de la Pera Francia. The house speciality is limon serrano, a rather good veal cutlet with a Fanny Craddock-like arrangement of orange and lemon segments and a gravy containing shards of crumbled tuna. The charcuterie and local hams are excellent – this is an area where pigs are supposedly fed on vipers. Grilled lamb is served with fine chips.

L AND D EVERY DAY £30–£35

CANDIDO

4

Plaza Axoguejo 5, Segovia (00) 34921425911

This immemorial tavern is situated virtually beneath the massive aqueduct. It has, perhaps, seen better days. Its suckling pig is flaccidly skinned and improbably tough. Battered hake with stewed peppers is all right; sweetbreads with a sort of mirepoix of garlic, leeks and carrots is devoid of seasoning. Finish with cheese marinated in fruity oil. A wine called Colegiata from the Toro region near Zamora is a bargain treat.

L AND D EVERY DAY £45+

El Burladero

1

Canalajas 1, Seville (00) 34954505599
Staid, carnal, pointlessly trad. Poor gazpacho, indifferent
oxtail, insipid pork shank, orange juice from a can, cream
from a spray can. For tourists only.

£80+

Enrique Becerra

5

Gamazo 2, Seville (00) 34954213049
Unpretentious bourgeois canteen, white napery, brown
panelling. Oxtail is done with pimenton, brains with garlic
and chilli, accompanied by rice cooked in garlic broth.
Good charcuterie.

L AND D MON TO SAT (CLOSED ALL DAY SUNDAY) £20

Maria Angeles

5

Puente de Triana, Seville (00) 34954337498
A Basque restaurant in a six-storey 19th-century pavilion that
rises from the riverside. First-rate grilled meats, potato gratin,
fish soup. The Austrian bean stew fabada is available.

£60

Parabere

6

Narcisso Campillo 4, Seville (no number listed)
Fashionable modern place whose floor has knives and forks
set into it. Cool staff, going on frosty. Imaginative cooking
of a sort that you might find in any major European city,
superior to 'genuine' Sevilliano stuff. Slow-cooked lamb,
deep-fried broccoli, veal steak with a glazed garlic puree,
marinated scallops with salmon roe. Good value.

£54

SWITZERLAND

GIANGROSSI   5
Rebgasse 8, Zurich (00) 4112412064
Cosy service and surroundings. The cooking veers between
extreme creaminess and enthusiastic acidulation.Tete de veau
is mugged by a too-vinegary dressing and jellied brawn is
accompanied by pickling liquid. Veal fricassee is rich, creamy,
but slightly insipid. The roesti is excellent.

L AND D TUES TO SAT £75

KRONENHALLE   6
Zollikerstrasse 214, Zurich (00) 4112516969
A delightful Zurich institution which has been going for
donkeys years and whose panelled walls are hung with
photographs of the city's notables, including James Joyce. The
dining rooms are sombre and elegant. Cooking is conservative
and well-made. Cold roast beef of real quality is served with
tartare sauce. Bratwurst, peppered steak and roesti are all
top-notch. The service is slightly superior.

L AND D EVERY DAY £65

USA

New England

BARTLEY'S

5

Kennebunkport, Maine (00) 12079675050

There's bad taste, then there's no taste. This tatty shack beside the Kennebunk estuary in a yacht village looks like it was last made over thirty years ago by a cheeseparing myope. The cheap carpet is threadbare, the cheap chairs are stained, the cheap prices make it a bargain. The only decorations are fairy lights and a little shrine to allegedly regular patron George Bush Snr, whose summer place is nearby. Still, better this than Major's Little Chef or Toni's Granita. The lobster stew, a sort of hunky, creamy chowder, is the works; it comes with crisp 'lobster' biscuits the size of a clam. Fried shrimp (langoustine) is done in breadcrumbs with good coleslaw and onion rings which make you see the point of that traduced dish.

ALL DAY EVERY DAY £35

BLANTYRE

6

16 Blantyre Rd, Lenox, Massachusetts (00) 14136373556

A stern-looking pile of c. 1900, which has been turned into a close approximation of the better sort of British country-house hotel. The place is furnished in a catholic mix of Second Empire, neo-Jacobean, Aubusson and palm court. It's close to Tanglewood, which may account for a harpist's presence. The cooking is what is to be expected of such an establishment – Frenchish, fairly refined, mostly accomplished. Rare venison is accompanied by a pithiviers pie of braised venison and apple; its elderflower sauce was too sweet. First-rate steak is herb-crusted – little beets alongside were insufficiently blanched and on the bitter side. Good fried foie gras, with chopped confit in a cabbage leaf and spiced cabbage; good French cheeses.

CLOSED SUN AND ALTERNATE MONDAYS AND TUESDAYS £125

THE LANDING

3

81 Front St, Marblehead, Massachusetts (00)17816311878

Pub beside the sound that separates the old port of Marblehead from Marblehead Neck, where the swanky villas are. Highly atmospheric bar peopled by 100 per cent proof sea dogs. The dining room is less fun but has the view. In case you're in any doubt of the place's nature, nylon sailcloth is stretched across the ceiling. The food is conscientiously prepared though short on delicacy. Caesar salad is a better bet than a bland salad with tuna carpaccio; steak with mash is all right; mussels in white wine suffer from an OD of lemon juice.

L AND D EVERY DAY £55

LEGAL SEA FOODS

5

Park Square, 201 Stuart St at Columbus Ave, Boston
(00) 16174264444
One link in a shortish chain of smart, well-priced, piscine
neo-brasseries. This one is large with a swirly bar and vinyl
banquettes, low-voltage lighting and high-performance service,
pale wood and plastic panels. A greaseless mix of deep-fried
scallops, clams, corncakes, calamari and haddock is impressive;
a rather bland chowder is OK comfort food; shrimp wontons
with soy sauce hit the spot.

L AND D EVERY DAY £60

POLLY'S PANCAKES

5

Route 117, Sugar Hill (00) 16038235575
A little piece of hick history, this. It's a long, rather wonky log
cabin belonging to the seventh generation of the Hildex maple
syrup dynasty. The views of maples, birches, clouds and
mountains are spectacular. And the accretion of gewgaws
within is appealing. Those who find maple syrup resistable
will nonetheless be impressed by the pancakes, which are
blini-like and expertly done in several varieties – with oatmeal
and buttermilk, with buckwheat, with walnuts, with cornmeal,
and so on. The rest of the cooking is upscale breakfast grub.

L AND D EVERY DAY £15+

RED LION INN

2

30 Main St, Stockbridge (00) 14132985545
Questionably trad New England cooking in an unquestionably
trad setting. The inn is ancient, wooden, with a verandah
where nutters mutter in rocking chairs and where gnarled
pumpkins of 1.5 metres diameter hint at what God's bollocks
must be like. An unusually lackadaisical waiter didn't seem
to know what succotash was – it is a mix of sweetcorn, kidney
beans and lobster served, in this instance, with polenta and
tarted up with oil infused with lobster and chilli; as rum as it
sounds. Veal pot roast was carelessly cooked; crude mash
flavoured with grain mustard.

L AND D EVERY DAY £90

WOODSTOCK INN AND RESORT   6
14 The Green, Woodstock, Vermont (00) 18024571100
The village is tiresomely cute. The hotel is large and
impersonal with countless gift shops selling the usual junk.
However, this wedding cake of a two-tier restaurant has a chef
whose 'new' American cooking is spirited and skilful. Flat bread
incorporating tomato and cheese is delightful, and the butter
on the table is like clotted cream. A crab cake bound with egg
was truly flavoured and fantastically light. Steak is sauced with
blue cheese, and served with a parsnip and cider (i.e., apple
juice) puree, sweet potatoes and pancetta. Chicken breast is
served with morels and a cheddar-flavoured potato gratin.

D EVERY DAY £70+

NEW YORK

21 CLUB   8
21 West 52nd St (00) 12125827200
The restaurant has a palpable air of mid-century chic. Walls
are loaded with Peter Arno cartoons, the ceiling is obliterated
by the football helmets, ice hockey helmets, models, etc., that
hang from it. Erik Blauberg's cooking is serious, correct,
scrupulously executed. Caesar salad is great; a mixed grill of
game – sausage, antelope stuffed with foie gras, rare rabbit
cutlets – was tremendous; steak was of stellar quality. The
wines are well chosen and frighteningly expensive.

L MON TO FRI, D MON TO SAT £160+

'44'   6
Royalton Hotel, 44 West 44th St (00) 12129448844
Philippe Starck's design has stood the test of time. This hotel
offers rooms you might actually like to live in, fantastic service,
the world's longest conversation pit and a restaurant that puts
substance before style. Breakfasts are excellent – pure pork
sausages, hash brown with peppers, good breads. The lunch
and dinner menus comprise unambitious but upscale dishes,
such as lobster risotto, steak with rosta – all of them neatly
enough cooked. Usefully quirky wine list.

L AND D EVERY DAY £150

AN AMERICAN PLACE
565 Lexington Ave (00) 12127152500

7

The staff wear horrible oatmeal linen jackets. The cooking is an allegedly modern take on traditional north-eastern dishes, and is generally well executed. Pot-roast short ribs were top-rate, served with delicious horseradish mash; foie gras comes with a sort of apple pie: it's not bad. The breads are ace.

B, L AND D EVERY DAY £170

BARNEY GREENGRASS
541 Amsterdam Ave at 86th St (00) 12127244707

6

One of the glories of gastronomic New York. A 92-year-old deli that is most famous for it's smoked sturgeon. But there are also several styles of smoked salmon, there is pastrami salmon, kippered salmon, matjes herrings, salted tongue... You can take out or have a plate of something there.

B AND L TUES TO SUN £35

CAFE DES ARTISTES
1 West 67th St (00) 12128773500

6

The exterior and lobby are similar to an English roadhouse and every bit as appealingly bogus. The dining rooms are splendid, if your idea of splendour is murals of coyly voluptuous nudes. The food is French with a mitteleurop twist. Pot au feu comprises succulent brisket, marrow bone, cabbage, turnip and potato; salt cod brandade is excellent; fried foie gras and roast chicken suffered from overcooking.

L AND D EVERY DAY £110+

CITY HALL
131 Duane St (00) 12122277777

4

A currently hottish ticket in Tribeca. The building is high Victorian with exposed structural irons, chunky banquettes, an open kitchen. The space is vast, vital, happening, buzzy. But... double chicken soup was an aggressive bath of dill; pot-roasted short ribs were marred by a sauce that went beyond Bovril.

L MON TO FRI, D MON TO SAT £100

GALLAGHER'S STEAK HOUSE
228 West 52nd St (00) 12122455336

6

An unrelentingly carnivorous joint, whose beef ribs are put to mature in an ageing room with a window onto the street. The food is piled even higher than the atmosphere. Caesar salad comes in a family-sized portion; a burger was of fine quality: charred without and red within, and apparently uncut with onion.

L AND D EVERY DAY £85

GRAMERCY TAVERN

9

42 East 20th St (00) 12124770777

Tom Colechio's cooking is technically faultless. He possesses a lightness of touch which is more European than American. The food is startlingly good. Recommended: wild mushroom tart; roast calf sweetbreads; beef – slow-braised cheek, rare steak and marrow bone covered with a perfect consommé; roast squab. There are a dozen or so bins by the glass.

L AND D EVERY DAY £130

GRAND CENTRAL'S OYSTER BAR

4

Grand Central Station, 42nd St (00) 12124906650

The rooms in the bowels of Grand Central Station are vaulted and tiled to look like basket-weave. The menu is compendious: 25 different types of oyster, every other bivalve you've heard of, countless crustacea, flat fish, river fish, smoked fish, kippered fish. There's chicken for the perverts.

L AND D MON TO SAT £75

ROBERTO'S

8

632 East 186th St, Bronx (00) 17187339503

The restaurant might have been airlifted from Naples; its customers might have been airlifted from Scorcese. It is a wedge-shaped room with terracotta walls hung with monochrome photographs. The cooking is simple and is executed with lightness and precision. Fondant rigatoni were sauced with a tomato-less ragu of veal, over which black truffle was grated in copious quantities; immensely savoury sausages come with broccoli rabe.

L TUES TO FRI, D TUES TO SUN £50

INDEX